PT Boat

by Henry B. Lent

"LIGHTWEIGHT SLUGGERS with the heavyweight punch!"
Six PT boats streak out to sea in column formation.

PT Boat

BOB REED WINS HIS COMMAND
AT MELVILLE

BY Henry B. Lent

*ILLUSTRATED WITH OFFICIAL PHOTOGRAPHS,
U. S. NAVY AND PHOTOGRAPHS TAKEN AT THE
MELVILLE BASE BY CARROLL VAN ARK*

NEW YORK · THE MACMILLAN COMPANY

1943

Binding design, Mosquito Fleet insigne, used by courtesy of Walt Disney Productions.

PRINTED IN THE UNITED STATES OF AMERICA.

Acknowledgments

They say the PT's get into your blood, and I believe it must be so. Certainly, during my stay at Melville, they got into mine.

Perhaps this happens because you realize that these mighty midgets—with the impudence and wallop of a Jack the Giant Killer—have no hesitation in attacking an enemy battleship a hundred times their own size. They can even knock a submarine out of the water—and fighter planes and bombers out of the sky!

But I think, even more than the boats themselves, it's the *men* that make you want to cheer the PT's—the officers and men of the Mosquito Fleet, who have already turned in one of the greatest fighting records in United States naval history.

So, in this book, I have tried to tell something of the story of what makes a PT fighting man.

It would be impossible for me to list the names of all the officers and men who can rightfully claim to have helped write this book. To all of them I am grateful.

Especially to Lieutenant Commander W. C. Specht, Commanding Officer of the Motor Torpedo Boat Squadrons Training Center at Melville. I am particularly grateful for his kindness in permitting me to draw so freely from the inspiring talks he has made from time to time to the men under his command. I knew no better way to present a true picture of what the Navy expects from a boy who volunteers for PT Squadrons service.

A most respectful bow, also, to the editor and staff of *The Skeeter—Shootin' the Breeze 'roun' Melville.* Various items appearing in this grand weekly PT newspaper helped provide color for the story of Bob Reed's training.

And, finally, to Lieutenant T. R. Stansbury, Senior Instructor, many thanks—for his patience, hospitality, and generous assistance during my stay at the Base.

HENRY B. LENT

Contents

Welcome to Melville

The Newport bus sped southward along the shore-line highway, high above Narragansett Bay.

For Ensign Bob Reed, U.S.N.R., this was the last lap of a journey that had started two days ago, following his graduation from the Midshipmen's School at Notre Dame.

The peaceful rolling countryside which he could see from the bus window—the old colonial farmhouses, the rambling stone fences, and the blue whitecapped bay down below—seemed a strange setting indeed for the exciting adventures which he knew awaited him.

For Bob Reed had been chosen from among many who had eagerly volunteered for training as student officers in Uncle Sam's famed Mosquito Fleet. And now it was only a matter of minutes until he would arrive at his destination—the Motor Torpedo Boat Squadrons Training Center, at Melville, Rhode Island.

For the thousandth time there flashed through his mind the heroic exploits of the officers who had gone before him —Bulkeley, Cox, Akers, Kelly, and the rest of gallant Squadron 3, whose names and glorious deeds in the Philippines were now recorded forever in naval history.

From the very beginning the swift hornetlike PT boats had fired Bob's imagination. More than anything else, he had hoped and prayed that he would be among the new officers chosen to uphold the proud traditions of the "Expendables." And his wish had been granted.

As he thought back over the events of the past few weeks, and the new life that lay before him, Bob suddenly noticed that some of his fellow passengers were preparing to get off the bus. All of them were sailors.

Bob leaned forward and asked one of them, "Are we coming to Melville?"

"Yes, sir," the bluejacket replied, "the bus will be pulling up to the Base gate in a couple of minutes."

The bus was already slowing down. Bob reached overhead and got his bag from the rack. As the bus rolled to a stop, he swung down onto the roadway. Facing him was a big sign which read: MOTOR TORPEDO BOAT SQUADRONS TRAINING CENTER—MELVILLE, R.I.

One of the sailors, realizing that Bob was a new incoming officer, pointed to the sentry booth about a hundred feet inside the main gate.

"You'll have to check in with the Marines, sir," he explained. "The Base will probably send a station wagon up the hill for you."

Bob thanked the seaman and walked down the road toward the sentry shack. Beyond the booth the hill dropped sharply, and the road wound down in sweeping curves to the edge of Narragansett Bay. Even from this distance

10

Bob could see the long sprawling barracks where the enlisted men were quartered, and the neat rows of curved-roof metal Quonset huts in which the officers lived.

The sailors who had come with Bob on the bus passed the sentry booth and started their long trek down the hill to the Base. Bob set down his bag, reached into his pocket for his Midshipmen's School credentials and handed them to the Marine who was on sentry duty.

The Marine glanced at them hastily, stepped inside his booth, and telephoned the Base headquarters. After a brief conversation he emerged from the shack.

"They'll send up for you immediately," he said.

When the station wagon arrived, Bob slung his bag in and took his place beside the driver. At the foot of the hill, the car pulled up in front of Hut 18.

"This is headquarters, sir," the driver said.

Bob thanked him and entered the hut. Seated at a desk in its spacious interior was a naval lieutenant, working over some papers. A small sign on his desk proclaimed that he was the Duty Officer. As Bob entered, the officer looked up.

Bob saluted briskly and announced, "Ensign Reed, sir, reporting for training," and he handed the O.D. his credentials and orders.

The officer read them carefully, then stood up and offered his hand to the newcomer.

"Glad to have you aboard, Reed," he said, with a very friendly smile. "We've been expecting you. A great many of the new class have already arrived." He paused, and ran his eye down a printed list that lay on the top of his desk. "Let's see," he said. "You've been assigned to Hut 27. You may go down there right now, if you'd like to."

Bob thanked him and hurried down to his quarters. He found that the five other tenants of Hut 27 had arrived before him. Several of them were still busy unpacking and stowing away their gear into the lockers. They all looked up as Bob came in.

"Hello, there," exclaimed a handsome six-footer who happened to be nearest the door. "My name's Warner— Bill Warner."

They shook hands. Bob identified himself and went through the round of introductions. Warner, he learned, was from Texas. One of the other boys was Ted Butler, All-American tackle from Purdue. The third bunkmate was Don Allen, famous Yale track star of '41. The remaining two were brothers—Al and Harvey Jordan, from Virginia. Their father, and his father before him, had been high-ranking naval officers, Bob learned later.

"Unpack your gear, Reed, and come on down to the docks with us," Warner said. "We want to look the boats over."

Bob unpacked in a matter of seconds and announced that he was all set to go. The six brand-new Ensigns strolled down past the long double row of Quonset huts to the lagoon.

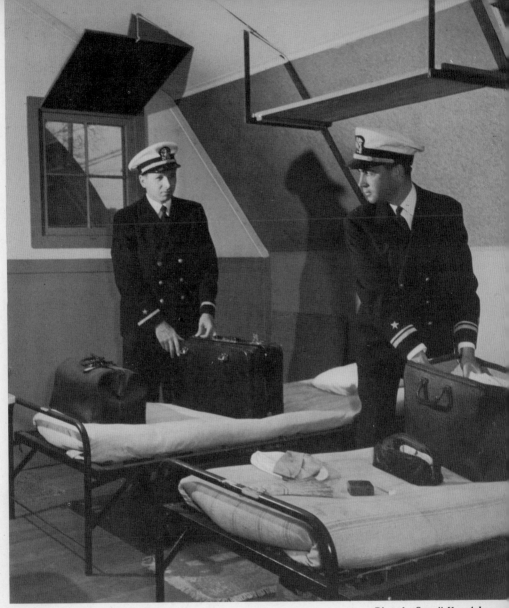

Photo by Carroll Van Ark

"WELCOME TO MELVILLE!" Two incoming officers unpack
their gear.

One of the motor torpedo boats was about to put out. As it nosed out from the dock, the skipper nudged his throttles slightly forward to gain headway. The deep-throated rumble of the boat's three great Packard engines, even at idling speed, sent out vibrations that could be distinctly felt some distance back from the dock.

"Listen to those babies talk!" Bill Warner exclaimed.

"Boy, what a boat!" Bob chimed in. "I can't wait till we go out on one!"

Now the long sleek PT boat was clear of the dock. The skipper advanced his throttles firmly and, with an ear-shattering blast from its six exhaust stacks, the gray motor torpedo boat shot out into the bay. Behind it trailed a white foamy wake as broad as a highway, and the propellers churned up a "rooster tail" plume ten feet high.

"Look at 'er streak through the water!" Ted Butler exclaimed, his eyes fairly popping in amazement at such unexpected speed.

"Sounds like three Navy planes in a power dive!" Al Jordan said as they watched the bulletlike PT boat grow smaller and smaller in the distance.

"Those engines pack plenty of power, all right," his brother Harvey added.

"I was reading a magazine article the other day that said they're actually aircraft-type engines," Don Allen said. "They're modern 12 cylinder versions of the Packard engines which Gar Wood used in his famous speedboat, *Miss America,* when he lifted the Harmsworth Trophy."

14

SNUGGED DOWN by the sea wall, beside their mother ship, these PT's are being readied for under-way maneuvers.

"I'm beginning to understand why it is that a midget Mosquito Boat can attack a Jap warship a hundred times its size and get away with it," Bill Warner added. "Trying to hit a zigging PT boat with an ordinary naval gun would be like trying to pick off a bumblebee with a Springfield rifle!"

The boys walked the length of the docks, looking over the many PT boats which were snugged down alongside. The speedy hard-hitting craft were actually much larger than any of the student officers had believed them to be. With their bristling antiaircraft turrets, Oerlikon guns, torpedo tubes, and depth charges, they were certainly more deadly in appearance than anything else anywhere near their size afloat.

"We sure were lucky to get into the PT Boat Squadrons!" Bob summed it up as they headed back for Hut 27.

"I'll say we were," Bill Warner agreed. "But I can see that we've got a tough time ahead of us."

"That's O.K. with me," Harvey Jordan remarked. "Nothing that happens from here on out will ever make me sorry I joined up with the Mosquito Fleet!"

HERE THEY COME—thundering down the bay under the
watchful eye of a Navy blimp!

"We Can Dish It Out"

That evening, after mess, the student officers and men of the new class filed into the Base auditorium to hear the Commanding Officer's speech of welcome.

The big hall was packed. Ensign Bob Reed and the other boys from Hut 27 sat together, near the front. The Commanding Officer, wearing the two and a half stripes of a Lieutenant Commander, sat on the platform flanked by his Executive Officer and several of the department heads. When he finally stood up to speak, a full minute passed while he quietly looked over the rows of faces before him.

"All of you probably know," he began, "that there are vast numbers of young men throughout the country and in the Fleet today who would give a great deal to have the opportunity which is now yours—that of qualifying to operate and fight the finest motor torpedo boats the world has ever produced."

The C.O. then explained why the requirements and standards for motor torpedo boat duty are necessarily high. He told them that every officer and every man on

18

board these small swift craft not only must have a thorough knowledge of his own duties but also must be completely familiar with the duties of every other man on board.

"For example," he said, with a smile, "the Ship's Cook must know his beans and be able to wash dishes; but he must *also* be able to navigate the boat, fire the guns and torpedoes, run the engines, and operate the radio. Nevertheless, we call him a cook!"

The Commanding Officer compared the PT boat crew with a well-trained football team.

"But there is one important difference with this eleven-man team," he cautioned his listeners. "When the whistle blows and the game starts, there are no substitutes and there's no coach sitting on the bench. If a player goes out, a teammate must take over the missing man's job as well as his own.

"Another thing," he went on, "this game is being played against professionals and they're plenty tough. They make up their own rules, and they change the rules without warning. I don't need to remind you that the stakes are high—for the stakes are Victory. And, in order to be in on the finish, we've got to play darn good ball!"

As Bob and his fellow officers listened to the Commanding Officer's talk, they realized more and more that there was no place for second-stringers in the Motor Torpedo Boat Squadrons. If there was any doubt in their minds, it vanished when the C.O. warned them that they must com-

19

plete an extremely rigid course of training within a period that was far too short for learning so much. . . .

"We cannot possibly turn out top-flight PT boat officers and men unless you put everything you've got into your work," he told them. "We can dish it out and, because this is the Navy, we can make you take it. But the final result rests with you alone."

At this point the Commanding Officer informed the boys that their instructors were a hand-picked group of officers, many of whom had already fought the enemy at Pearl Harbor, in the Philippines, and at Midway. They had returned to the Base to pass on to others the benefit of their experiences.

In closing, the C.O. said, "I want you all to enjoy your work and your stay here. True, we are strict in our requirements and we expect a great deal of you. But no more than you are capable of doing.

"If, at any time, you feel that the work, the discipline, or even the weather is getting you down, just remember that many hundreds have gone through Melville before you and have gone out where the going is really tough. They did not fail us—and you must not fail them.

"I sincerely hope that in two months' time, when you have completed your course of training, each and every one of you here today will have proven that you measure up in every way to the finest and the toughest striking force the Navy has ever produced—the most dependable, *unexpendable* Motor Torpedo Boat Squadrons!"

HUT INSPECTION—and everything shipshape!

As the "Old Man" finished his talk, the boys in the assembly hall gave him a round of applause that left no doubt as to their firm resolve to live up to the standards he had set for them.

Following the Commanding Officer's speech there was a brief talk by the Executive Officer of the Base, and by several of the chief instructors. One of the officers, who was now stationed at the Base as Chief Gunnery Instructor, had served with Lieutenant Commander Bulkeley in the Philippines.

The Senior Instructor also had a few words to say. First he wrote down on the blackboard a list of the personnel who made up the crew of each motor torpedo boat, like this:

2 Commissioned Officers
> Boat Captain
> Executive Officer

9 Enlisted Men
> 1 Gunner's Mate
> 1 Torpedoman
> 1 Radioman
> 1 Quartermaster
> 3 Engineers
> 1 Cook
> 1 Seaman

Then he described briefly the training they would get at the Base. The training, he explained, was divided into four main subjects: (1) Gunnery, which also included

22

PT SQUADRON TACTICS and training cruises are all scheduled in advance, here in the Operations Office.

torpedoes, depth charges, and smoke-screen technique; (2) Seamanship and Navigation; (3) Communications, which included radio, visual signaling, and tactics; and (4) Engineering, which was a course on the boat's engines.

"There are three types of courses given in each of these subjects," the Senior Instructor added. "They are known as the A course, the B course, and the C course. The man who takes the A course in any subject gets the works! That's the advanced course. The B course offers fewer hours of instruction, and the C course is still shorter."

Then he explained that each man would get A courses in the subjects he must know best. For example, sailors who were training to become PT boat engineers would take the A course in Engineering, and the B or C courses in Gunnery and Navigation. Gunner's mates would, of course, specialize in Gunnery. Every officer, however, must take A or B courses in *all* subjects.

When the assembly was dismissed, each boy was given a printed schedule of instruction for the coming week.

"Well, we certainly take the plunge tomorrow," Bob remarked as the student officers drifted back into Hut 27 and sat down to study their schedules over more carefully.

"Yep, Gunnery's first on the list—the A course—at 8:10 tomorrow morning," Ted Butler said. "Boy, my trigger finger's itching to draw a bead on a moving target with one of those .50 caliber antiaircraft guns."

AT BETTER THAN A MILE A MINUTE a PT streaks
through the water with men at their battle stations.

"Then you'd better control that itch, Ted," was Bill Warner's rejoinder. "All we get tomorrow is classroom stuff—finding out what makes those popguns stutter so pretty."

"I guess you're right, at that," Ted agreed sadly.

It was a disappointment to the young Ensigns to realize that they would spend most of their first month of training as landlubbers, but they knew there were many things they must learn before they could hope to be "under way" on the boats they would eventually command.

"It's sort of like Ground School at a Naval Aviation Training Station," Don Allen said. "My brother Joe is down at Pensacola working for his wings as a naval aviator. He wrote back that they didn't even fly in a plane the first month."

"Well, I guess that's the way it has to be," Bob said. "But it's sure going to be tough to sit in a classroom studying a manual and hear those PT boats buzzing around out there in the bay."

The discussion of the schedule went on for another hour or more.

Suddenly Al Jordan glanced at his wrist watch and exclaimed, "Say, we'd better quit shooting the breeze and turn in!"

"Golly, you're right!" his brother agreed. "I hadn't realized it was so late."

A few minutes later, just as the last man in Hut 27 tumbled into his bunk, the Base loud-speaker sounded its rasping "Lights out . . . Lights out!" and in all the huts up and down each narrow street the lights flicked out for the night.

Back to School

The alarm clock perched on top of Bob Reed's locker pointed to 8:10.

For almost two hours, ever since "Reveille," the Training Base had been bustling with activity. Groups of upperclassmen were already gathering on the docks, preparing to get under way on their day's maneuvers in the motor torpedo boats.

The warm sun was just beginning to burn off the early-morning haze that blanketed Narragansett Bay as Bob and his classmates hurried down Avenue A to the Gunnery classroom. Bill Warner cast an envious eye toward the docks, where the PT boats were beginning to throb and rumble.

"That will be us, a month from now," he said.

"Yes, if we don't wash out before we get that far," Bob ventured.

"That's a cheerful thought," Bill said, with a grin.

One by one the boys filed into the Gunnery classroom for their first hour and a half of instruction. After a short introductory talk the Gunnery Instructor went on to ex-

"GETTING THE ONCE-OVER"—commissioned officers
line up for inspection.

plain the armament of the motor torpedo boats, stressing how important it was for the boys to understand thoroughly the operation of the heavy antiaircraft turret guns with which each boat was equipped.

Starting with one of the deadly .50 caliber machine guns, he showed them its firing mechanism and named each separate part. Later, he explained, they would practice clearing up jams and stoppages, and would learn all about the gun turrets.

"But before you start actual target practice, I want you to know these guns from A to Z," the instructor said. "Before I finish with you, I want you to be able to dismount the guns in the dark and reassemble them by touch."

He ran his hand lovingly down the perforated muzzle of one of the .50 caliber machine guns.

"We'll start on this baby," he said, and the boys grouped closely about him so as not to miss a thing he showed them.

The minutes flew by as the Gunnery Instructor got deeper into the subject he knew so well.

It seemed to Bob that the class had scarcely started when the instructor glanced up at the wall clock and announced, "Well, that's all we'll have time for today. Next time we will review today's work and then start in on the 20 millimeter Oerlikon gun—the rapid-fire antiaircraft gun that's mounted aft on the deck of some PT boats."

Photo by Carroll Van Ark

WHAT PUTS THE BUZZ in a Mosquito boat? Three Packard supermarine engines, patterned after the racing engines
that helped the speedboat *Miss America* win the Gold Cup.

From their first lesson in Gunnery, the Ensigns made their way down the street to the Communications classroom.

The instructor, Lieutenant Walker, first explained briefly the various things they would have to learn. He reminded them that, even though the radiomen on the PT boats were given a much more complete course than the officers would get, even the officers must qualify in code and semaphore signaling, and must be able to send and receive messages at a high rate of speed.

On the walls of the Communications hut were pictures of the dot-and-dash flag alphabet, in which each letter was represented by a flag. There were also many special flags and pennants used in signaling "Formation," "Speed," "Position," "Emergency," and other naval signals.

Toward the end of the instruction period the officer put several of the Ensigns through their paces at semaphore signaling, a subject which they had already studied at the Midshipmen's schools. When Bob's turn came, the instructor interrupted him in the middle of the message he was sending.

"No, no, Reed," he said impatiently. "You're blurring your characters. Put some snap into it. Make each motion distinct, with a longer pause between characters. Now, then, stand erect, feet together and arms straight. Pretend that you have no elbows."

Once more Bob wigwagged the message, this time to the complete satisfaction of the instructor.

Courtesy Packard Motor Car Company

HERE'S WHAT A PACKARD PT ENGINE looks like when it's completely torn down. Many a PT boat Engineer can put it together again blindfolded!

When the Communications class was over, the boys picked up their manuals and trudged down the street to the big building that sheltered the Engineering School. This building was larger than all the others—"sort of a grandpappy Quonset hut," as Bill Warner put it.

The Chief Petty Officer who was in charge of the school greeted his new class cordially and led them on a tour of inspection. Mounted on portable dollies were five or six big Packard marine engines in various stages of teardown and assembly. One was a cutaway engine, with sections of the crankcase, cylinder walls, timer housing, and other vital parts cut away so that the internal parts could be studied in slow motion as the engine turned over.

The boys inspected the brute 12 cylinder supermarine engines with admiration. Each engine was more than six feet in length—just about the biggest, most powerful high-test gasoline engine any of them had ever seen.

Bob moved back from the group a few steps so that his eye could take in the whole engine.

"So this is what puts the buzz in the Mosquito Boats!" he said.

"Right!" the instructor replied. "It's a lot of engine, isn't it? When you gear up three of these monsters in a plywood Elco or Higgins hull, you know you're really making knots over the water!"

He explained that the Ensigns would get much of the same classroom work that would be given to the engineers. As officers, however, they would wind up their course

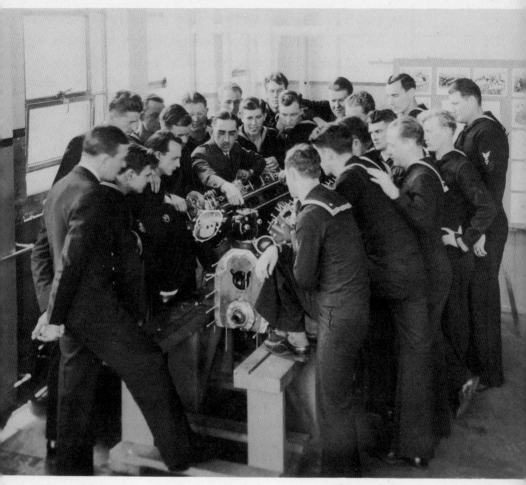

MANY PT OFFICERS and Squadron Engineers go through
the Packard Marine Engine School, where they learn about
PT boat engines from the men who built them.

with only one day of teardown and assembly of engines, whereas the engineers would spend two solid weeks or more on assembly and repair work.

"We don't expect our commissioned officers to be able to assemble a Packard marine engine with their eyes closed," the instructor assured them.

"Can PT boat engineers do that?" Bill Warner asked.

"Well, not at first," the Chief Petty Officer admitted. "But each of my five assistant instructors can. In fact, they'll bet you twenty-five dollars to a dime that they can scramble up all the parts of one of these engines and put 'em back together again blindfolded."

One of the students gave a low whistle, in amazement.

"However," the instructor quickly added, "I'd advise you not to take them up on that, for you'd lose!"

At the end of the period he gave them each a thick manual covering the maintenance and operation of the PT boat engines.

"And this manual wasn't printed just for book collectors," he said. "It's meant to be *studied!*"

As the boys left the Engineering building, Don Allen groaned, "Whew! My head's buzzing already when I think of what we have to learn here the first month!"

"This is just a preview, Sonny Boy," Bill Warner chuckled. "Seamanship and Navigation come next."

"Bring 'em on!" Bob Reed challenged. "We may be groggy, but they haven't got us hanging on the ropes yet!"

Things Columbus Never Knew

The A course in Seamanship and Navigation, although difficult, turned out to be one of the most popular periods in the new Ensigns' training.

Using the thick manual which had been prepared by their instructor, Lieutenant Howell, the boys waded into a long list of subjects which included Rules of the Road, Lights, Boat Handling, Under-Way Steering Rules, Compasses and Charts, and Theory of Navigation.

"Ever since man first went to sea," the instructor told them, "he has been struggling for the best possible answer to one important question: 'Where am I now, and where do I go from here?'

"At first, when man's rambles took him only a few miles from his home, alongshore in familiar areas, he had no trouble finding his way back. But as his curiosity took him farther and farther from places he knew, he discovered that, without some method of figuring out his position, he was literally 'at sea.' "

Lieutenant Howell then described the basic method of plotting "lines of position," by sighting three heavenly bodies. He drew a diagram on the blackboard showing how the intersection of the three lines gives the navigator his position, or *fix*.

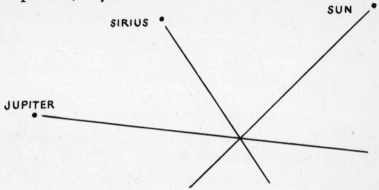

At this point one of the student officers asked why there was a difference between the length of a *statute* mile and that of a *nautical* mile.

"That's a very interesting question," Lieutenant Howell replied. "The globe is measured by imaginary lines called *parallels of latitude* and *meridians of longitude*."

He turned to the globe on his desk, showing how latitude is measured by parallel lines North and South from the Equator.

"But there was no central line, like the Equator, running from the North Pole to the South Pole, from which distances could be measured. And, down through the centuries, no one could agree just which meridian should be used for the starting point, when measuring longitude, East and West. Finally Britain, being Mistress of the Seas, decided that the meridian which passed through the

THEY LEFT SCHOOL to join the Navy. Now they're in the Navy
and back to school they go!

Greenwich Observatory, in London, should be the starting point, or 0 degrees longitude."

Turning to the student who had asked the question about the nautical mile, the instructor said, "And that brings us, finally, to the answer to your question. Having picked the meridian which passed through London as the all-important line from which to measure distance East and West, Britain also decided that the standard length of a mile should be equal to one minute (1') of longitude at the latitude of the Greenwich Observatory in London. This happened to be 5280 feet; so the British wrote it into their statutes as a legal mile, and it became known as the statute, or land, mile.

"But there were certain sailors who thought that was the wrong way to measure a mile. They insisted that a mile should equal one minute of longitude at the Equator—or 6080 feet. And they won out. So, today, 6080 feet is the accepted standard of measure for one nautical mile."

Getting back to the theory of navigation, the instructor reminded the boys that, when they finally went into combat zones as PT boat officers, they would often have to at-

Photo by Carroll Van Ark

WHAT A FIX a PT boat navigator would be in if he couldn't
find his fix! These boys are learning how.

tack the enemy under weather conditions that would keep most small craft tied up snugly at their moorings.

"You will quickly learn that rain squalls, thick weather, and dense fog give you better protection than a battery of antiaircraft guns," he said. "A PT boat is hard for the enemy to spot even under ideal weather conditions, because it's so small and so fast—and when the visibility is poor you get an even better break. Of course, it's more difficult to take your bearings in that kind of going," he added. "Very often you'll have to depend entirely upon *apple-tree* navigation, especially when operating in areas with which you are familiar."

Noting the puzzled expressions which greeted his last remark, Lieutenant Howell hastened to explain.

"Apple-tree navigation means exactly what it sounds like," he said. "For example, let us suppose that you are coming up the bay for the Base when pea-soup fog closes in. Rounding the point, you pick up some familiar object on the shore which you recognize—perhaps an apple tree, or a tumble-down farm shed, which tells you instantly that you're standing offshore, say, two hundred yards. Sometimes the apple-tree bearing will be the barking of a Newfoundland dog which you know lives at a certain farmhouse; or, a farmer calling in his cows. It is very important that you develop a keen sense of observation. You never know when some trifling incident you noticed in the past will save your skins in an emergency."

He then recounted an experience to illustrate his point.

Photo by Carroll Van Ark

A GROUP OF ENLISTED MEN brush up on Communications before going out on tactical maneuvers.

"Just before the war started," he said, "I spent a number of months aboard one of the Government's geodetic survey ships, charting the coast lines in the Arctic. Very often, because of foul weather and poor visibility, we had to rely solely on apple-tree navigation."

Lieutenant Howell told the boys that the surveying party soon learned the various spots along the coastal mountains where great flocks of auks nested. They also discovered that auks always used to fly out very high over the water to a distance of four miles, fill their crops with red shrimp, and fly back, low, to their nesting grounds. Thus, even when the ship's crew could not see land, if they saw the auks in flight they could judge their position and the direction in which land lay, by estimating the height at which the auks were flying.

The PT boat student officers found the Seamanship and Navigation course more and more interesting as they went along. Their instructor told them many useful facts about the operation of the boats themselves.

"Good PT boat handling," he cautioned them, "results from three factors: (1) Common sense, (2) proper instruction, and (3) experience. Common sense," he added, "is something which no amount of teaching will give you, unless you already have it. We do our best to give you proper instruction. Then you go out with an operating squadron, and experience alone determines whether you use these first two factors to become a good PT boat officer or just another dock smasher!"

A SEAMAN on the leading PT wigwags instructions to the other
boats in the division.

In PT boat handling, he told them, the part played by good seamanship is very important, because of the boat's small size, its high speed, and the ease with which it can be damaged by the action of the seas.

"It's impossible," he continued, "to combine the seaworthiness of a round-bottomed sailing vessel with the speed of a *Miss America*. The Navy's PT boats can outrun anything that floats and they carry weapons big enough to sink the biggest warship ever built, but great skill is required to operate them successfully. In short, the PT boat is a cross between a bucking horse and a streamlined pile driver. But remember that the sea is bigger and more powerful than anything that floats!"

The boys were particularly interested in methods of meeting "common emergencies" at sea. They were instructed how to hoist a jury rig, so that they could bring the PT boat home into port under sail if need be. And, in case they were forced to take to the life raft, they learned how to use the equipment which might be the means of saving their lives—charts, navigation tables, sextant, and hand compass. Lieutenant Howell also gave them useful hints on how to survive as castaways—how to squeeze fresh water out of a fish, how to sustain life on the vegetation they might find on deserted islands, and how to build crude shelters to protect them from the weather.

At the end of the instruction period Lieutenant Howell made a brief announcement that almost brought the boys to their feet cheering.

46

"It is customary," he said, "for the officers and men in each new class to go out on a short familiarization cruise during their first week here at the Base. Your division will report to the skipper of Motor Torpedo Boat Number 176 tomorrow morning at 8:10 sharp."

As the boys made their way back to their quarters, Bob Reed remarked, "They've certainly beefed up that S and N course with a lot of stuff that will come in handy when we get out with our squadrons."

"You said it," Bill Warner responded. "And, speaking of wringing out a fish to get fresh water, right now I'd rather have an ice-cold coke. How about it?"

There were Coca-Cola dispensers spotted here and there all over the Base. The Ensigns detoured to the nearest one and dropped their nickels into the slot.

Bill held up his bottle and proposed a toast.

"Here's to us—under way—tomorrow!"

"Here's to us!" Don Allen repeated. "May the waves on Narragansett Bay all be little ones!"

"Stand the Tube Watch"

The next day dawned bright and clear.

Bundled up in their under-way gear, the boys from Hut 27 joined the other student officers of their division on the dock where Motor Torpedo Boat 176 was tied up, shortly after 8:00.

Although the weather was not cold, each of them wore two heavy Navy sweaters, a helmet, and a waterproof jacket with parka hood.

"I feel like a member of the Byrd Antarctic Expedition," Bob said as he adjusted his helmet strap.

"You do look something like a penguin, at that," Harvey Jordan remarked.

"We'll probably be glad we're so well padded when we start whipping down the bay at better than a mile a minute," Ted Butler added.

The skipper of PT Boat 176 was already aboard. He was busy on the flying bridge, standing in the control cockpit, making a last-minute checkup. Beside him was his executive officer. Both were Ensigns, attached to the Melville Motor Torpedo Boat Squadrons Base.

One by one the student officers clambered aboard the long streamlined warcraft. There was room for about ten of them in the open cockpit. The others clustered behind them in a group. A seaman handed each man a kapok life jacket.

"The bay is pretty smooth this morning," the Executive Officer said, "but put on these life jackets just the same. A man overboard is a lot easier to fish out if he has a life jacket on."

The skipper announced that, when they got under way, each student officer would be given a turn at the wheel.

"Those who are awaiting their turn either may watch what's going on or may make a tour of the boat," he said. "Ask all the questions you want. The purpose of this run is to familiarize you with the PT boat."

After making certain that his three throttles were in "Neutral," he signaled the engineers, below, to start the engines. Standing close beside the skipper, Bob watched every move with close attention.

Now the giant Packard engines were rumbling at idling speed. A seaman scampered forward, then aft, as the lines were cast off.

The skipper slowly advanced the three throttle knobs with the heel of his palm. The engine-telegraph slot just ahead of each throttle changed from "Neutral" to "Ahead."

"That's the signal to the engine room to shift gears," he explained to the student officers grouped about him.

49

"The throttle control is from the bridge, but the engineers shift the gears. There are only three positions: Neutral, Ahead, and Astern."

The needle on the r.p.m. dial crept higher as the PT boat swung out from the dock into the bay. The rumbling of the engines increased to a steady staccato drumming.

One of the student officers gazed anxiously ahead out toward the bay, where now an occasional whitecap was breaking the blue surface of the water.

Turning to the skipper, he asked, "If we should get seasick, what should we do?"

Bob had been wondering the same thing, but was glad that somebody else had asked the question.

"Oh, you won't get sick on a calm day like this," the skipper answered. "But if you do, just stand the tube watch."

The Executive Officer smiled and pointed to one of the long torpedo tubes mounted on the deck alongside the cockpit.

"He means to step outside, bend over that, and forget your party manners," he grinned. "But always to leeward!" he added as an afterthought.

The rest of the boys laughed when the reason for that precaution dawned on them.

Now the PT boat was skimming over the water at three-quarter throttle. Bob glanced back at the broad white wake and the foamy geyser thrown up by the three propellers.

"STAND BY FOR ACTION!" The skipper, with hand on throttle, is ready to speed his craft toward the target.

"Stand by to take over in a few minutes, Reed," the boat captain said as he headed the boat down the bay.

He explained the "Orders to the Helmsman" as given on a PT boat. He reminded the new officers that in naval service the old orders "Port your helm" and "Starboard your helm" were no longer used. Those terms were too confusing, and dated back to sailing-ship days when boats had old-fashioned tillers. In those days, "Port your helm," actually meant "Right rudder," which was very misleading. For this reason, even the merchant marine had dropped the use of these terms in 1935. The present-day orders, the skipper said, are simply "Right rudder," which means "Direct the boat's bow to starboard," and "Left rudder," which means "Direct the boat's bow to port." He also explained that the boat would turn *with* the wheel, just like an automobile.

Suddenly he moved the throttles full forward. The engines emitted a blasting roar. The stern of the PT boat dug down into the water as the three screws drove it forward at terrific speed. The bow rose up as the water "packed" underneath the hull. Now it was planing on the surface like a speedboat. The wind whistled with galelike force. Spray stung the boys' faces like sleet.

The skipper's hand closed firmly on the "speed knob," which was fastened to the rim of the wheel, and flung back over his shoulder, "Everybody hang on!"

Then, with the boat racing ahead at full throttle, he suddenly whirled the wheel around hard to the right. Banking

PROUDLY DISPLAYING its famed Mosquito Boat insignia, a PT boat opens up its Packard engines for high-speed maneuvers.

like a racing car on a turn, the PT boat slewed around in a sharp lightning U turn that left the boys fairly gasping for breath. The long metal radio antenna, standing upright like a buggy whip in its socket, bent over almost to the water, pulled by the centrifugal force of the boat's motion.

Some of the boys let out a yell on the turn, the way many people do when they shoot downward and around curves on a roller coaster. Never before had they seen such speed and maneuverability in a boat!

Coming out of the turn, the skipper cut down his r.p.m.'s and motioned for Bob to take the wheel.

Bob's heart was pounding like a trip hammer with excitement as he took a firm grasp on the spokes.

"Keep her down to about twenty-five knots," the skipper said, "and hold a course for that tip of land that juts out, about five miles ahead."

The smooth rhythmic roar of the engines gave Bob a sense of the terrific power now at his command. To him, the speed of the motor torpedo boat seemed more like the sensation of flight than did actual flying in a plane.

The skipper reached past him and advanced the throttles another inch. The PT boat responded instantly, leaping ahead with express-train speed over the bay.

The skipper glanced at the r.p.m. dial.

"Now you're making a good fifty-five knots," he shouted, above the roar of the engines. "Put her into a turn."

Bob grabbed the knob on the rim of the wheel. It looked

54

so easy when the skipper did it! Would the PT boat respond as readily for him? Bob braced himself and spun the wheel around all the way to the left. The boat shot into the turn, riding the steep bank created by its own motion through the water. At the completion of the U turn, Bob pulled back his throttles and relinquished the helm to the skipper. What a boat!

"Who's next?" the Executive Officer asked.

The skipper motioned for Don Allen to take over.

As the boat got under way once again, Bob swung down out of the cockpit into the chartroom. Then he climbed down another short ladder and walked forward past a thick bulkhead into the crew's quarters. Here there were nine bunks, one for each man in the crew. Adjoining the crew's quarters, amidships, were two roomy cabins for the skipper and his executive officer . . . then a complete galley, with refrigerator and electric stove . . . then a dayroom, with a big table, phonograph, and bookshelves. This was where the PT boatmen could lounge and take things easy when off duty.

Next, ducking down a short companionway, Bob found himself in the engine room. Never before had he seen an engine room so spotless! The huge Packard engines were as clean and shiny as new cars on a showroom floor. It seemed hard to believe that three engines so spotlessly clean could make such a racket! They sounded almost like a formation of planes taking off together.

The three engineers were too busy to give Bob more

than a passing glance, for the PT boat was now churning through the water at close to top speed. All three men were watching their gauges intently, prepared to open their sea-water cooling scoops instantly if their engine temperatures started to climb. Each engineer sat with the engine almost "in his lap," his legs spread wide and braced, hanging on for life! Bob smiled to himself as he thought how much they looked like the trotting-horse drivers he'd seen at State Fairs, sitting astride their racing sulkies.

Suddenly, without a moment's warning, the PT boat swung into a tight turn, banking like a plane around a pylon. The engineers calmly "rode" their engines, leaning like motorcycle racers on a turn. The force of the boat's maneuver almost threw Bob against the bulkhead. Luckily he had a firm grasp on one of the many handrails and was able to stay on his feet.

As the boat slowed down, Bob climbed up out of the engine room, through the chart and radio room, and back onto the flying bridge. Don Allen, his face reddened by the wind and spray, was just giving the wheel back to the skipper, so that the next Ensign might take his turn.

Another half-hour passed. The PT boat streaked up and down the bay until finally each of the student officers had had an opportunity to handle it. Then the skipper took over for the run up the bay to the Base.

Just as they were getting under way, another MTB shot by them at terrific speed. The skipper accepted the friendly challenge. Advancing his throttles steadily, PT

A FUTURE PT BOAT SKIPPER under way for the first time.
He soon learns that a PT boat is amazingly responsive, in spite of
its terrific speed.

Boat 176 gave chase. Cutting over into the smooth core of the leading boat's wake, the skipper opened his throttles wide. So great was its speed that the water hissing past its hull sounded like bacon sizzling in a frying pan. The boys yelled excitedly and cheered their craft onward. The crew of the first PT boat waved back derisively. Apparently they knew the race was "in the bag," even though the distance between the two boats was growing shorter and shorter. But the first boat clearly had too great a lead to start with. It pulled into the lagoon a scant five seconds ahead of Number 176.

"My legs feel a little wobbly," Bill Warner said as the boys straggled back from the dock to their hut.

"So does my stomach," Bob admitted sheepishly.

"Mine, too," said Ted Butler.

"What a ride!" Al Jordan exclaimed. "I always thought I was a pretty fair sailor, but now . . . I'm beginning to wonder." He made a wry face.

"Cheer up, Al!" his brother replied. "We did pretty well for landlubbers. After a few more doses of it, we'll be able to take it along with the best of them. Now that you mention it, I'll confess that I felt a little green around the gills after some of those zig turns."

As they shed their under-way gear and got ready for their 10:15 class, the boys all agreed that nothing they had ever experienced could equal the thrill of that first motor torpedo boat ride.

58

Photo by Carroll Van Ark

ONE OF THE RAREST pictures ever taken at Melville—
PT crews "At ease!" Actually they are waiting to report for
under-way operations.

For Twenty-twenty Eyes Only

Walking rapidly along the path to the classroom hut with his companions, Bob Reed kept mumbling under his breath.

"B-24 . . . Liberator bomber . . . hundred and ten. B-17 . . . Flying Fortress bomber . . . hundred and six. PBY . . . Catalina patrol bomber . . . hundred and . . . hundred and . . ." He turned to Bill Warner and asked, "What's the wingspan of the Catalina, Bill?"

"A hundred and four, I think," Bill replied.

"Yeah, that's right," Bob agreed. "Golly, I thought I had them all cold by now."

"You should have," said Ted Butler. "You've even been saying them in your sleep."

"Well, this Plane Recognition course is no pipe," Bob remarked as they filed into Hut 17 and took their places.

Each student officer had been given a set of photographs of all present-day combat planes, including Axis planes as well as British and American, with diagrams and drawings. They not only had to learn to identify each plane instantly but also had to give its Army or Navy designation, its name and type and wingspan.

60

"No matter how good a gunner a man may be," the instructor said, "he's no good to the PT Boat Squadrons unless he can identify his target *in a split second*—and then hit it. Some of today's fighter planes can dive faster than the speed of sound itself," he continued. "It's a frightening sensation when you realize this for the first time, as I did when I was a gunner's mate on an MTB off Guadalcanal. A Jap Zero power-dived us when we were on patrol; and the sound of its engine came trailing along after it, the way a clap of thunder follows a streak of lightning. If you expect to come out of this war with a whole skin, speed in identifying your target is all-important."

By way of illustrating his point he started schooling the boys by means of the Renshaw system. He flashed pictures of various planes on a screen, one at a time, holding each one for the space of a single second. In that instant the student gunner was supposed to identify the plane and then was given time to write down its designation and type, its name and wingspread.

As the boys became more expert at spotting the planes quickly, the instructor cut down the length of time to half a second, then to a quarter of a second.

"Before you can pass this course," he told them, "you must be able to identify any plane I show you in one-twenty-fifth of a second. Now you understand why only men with perfect eyes can expect to make the grade for service in the PT Boat Squadrons."

In addition to the recognition of combat planes, the course included recognition of all types of Allied and Axis surface vessels and submarines. The boys were taught how to tell the various types of warships by their hull shape and general outline; by their gun turrets, number of stacks, and position of the bridge.

"Every PT boat officer must be able to identify all types of surface vessels, and their nationality, the minute he sights them," the instructor said. "Usually, when you know the *type* of ship, you can determine its probable mission and the location of other units in the force."

He went on to explain that battleships seldom operate alone but are usually found near the center of a formation, with a ring of destroyers guarding them against attack. Destroyers, on the other hand, are sometimes found singly, on a scouting mission or on the outer circle of a large group. Sometimes, of course, destroyers travel in groups, by themselves. Cruisers, when in formation, ordinarily travel about halfway from the center to the outer edge. Sometimes single cruisers operate on independent scouting or raiding missions. And submarines are found either operating singly or working together in big "wolf packs" in the shipping lanes.

"Sometimes the difference between various nations' warships is very slight," the instructor added. "There is a case on record where a formation of Jap Zeros attacked one of their own destroyers and sank it. And a very agreeable sight it was to our PT Boat Squadron! But see to it

"NOW YOU SEE IT—now you don't!" A class in aircraft recognition learns to tell one plane from another in a split second.

that none of you men make a mistake like that! Always be sure of your target—*then* always be sure you hit it!"

That afternoon, after midday mess, all the boys in Bob's division went to near-by Price's Neck for their first machine-gun practice. Here, under the supervision of a gunner's mate, they took turns firing at a sleeve target, which was towed back and forth in front of the gunnery range by one of the planes from the Quonset Naval Air Station.

As each man's turn came he took his position at one of the machine-gun mounts. Then, as the target plane began its run and drew abreast of the range, the gunner's mate would give the order "Stand by to fire," then . . . "Fire!"

The first time up, Bob Reed failed to allow sufficient lead on his moving target. Since every fifth bullet was a fiery tracer, he could clearly see that his line of fire was trailing off behind the sleeve. He tried to correct his mistake, but it was too late. He had already spent his allotted twenty rounds of ammunition.

The next time up, however, he shot *ahead* of the moving target, and could see the stream of machine-gun bullets ripping through the white cloth.

Even as the staccato blast of the gun echoed back from the bay, the tow plane banked and turned again for the return run and the next officer in line stepped up to the mount. Each man in the division was given an opportunity to fire twenty rounds twice.

Later that afternoon, just as the Ensigns arrived back at the Base, the loud-speaker rasped out its now-familiar

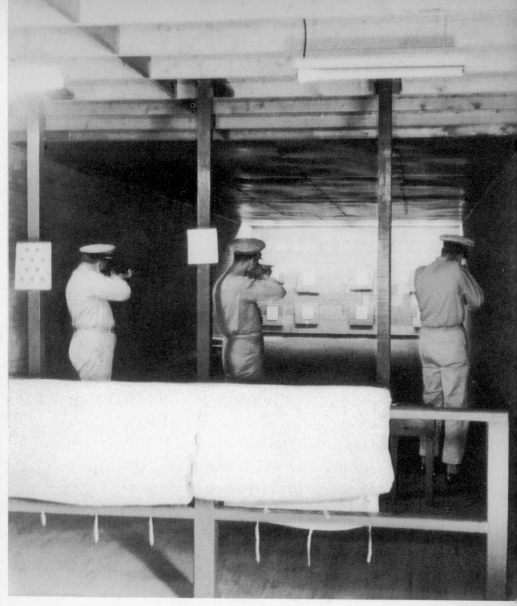

Photo by Carroll Van Ark

"JUST LIKE CONEY ISLAND!"—PT boat Ensigns try their skill at the Base rifle range.

"Now hear this!" Whenever the Duty Officer had an announcement to make, he always started with those words —to make certain that no one would miss hearing what he had to say.

"Now hear this!" he barked. "All student officers in Division A will report at 1800, in Hut 23, for classroom gunnery practice." He repeated the announcement once more.

"Golly, that means us!" Bob said.

"That *would* happen just when I was planning to spend the whole evening boning up on my navigation!" Al Jordan exclaimed. "What's this classroom gunnery business about, anyway?"

"I don't know," Bill Warner said, "but we'll soon find out."

Immediately after mess the boys trailed over to Hut 23. Classroom gunnery practice, they discovered, meant shooting with an electric machine gun at the image of a moving plane on a motion-picture screen.

After the instructor had explained just how it was done, the boys manned their guns.

With his finger on the trigger Bob trained his machine gun on the screen, waiting for the "enemy" to appear. Suddenly, diving from a background of clouds, a Jap Zero swooped across the screen in a sharp bank. Bob squeezed the trigger. Much to his surprise, a bell started to ring!

"You opened fire too soon, Reed," the instructor cau-

Photo by Carroll Van Ark

"LEAD THAT TARGET!" A gunner's mate tries his hand
at the deadly Oerlikon antiaircraft gun.

tioned him. "Hold your fire until the plane is in your sights. If this were the real thing, that Jap would now be plugging *you*—after that miss!"

When the next plane broke through the cloud bank on the screen, Bob waited until it filled his sights. Then he opened fire. This time his gun gave out a loud *da-da-da-da* noise, something like that of a real machine gun, and a target ring of light on the screen told him that he had scored a direct hit.

To make the classroom gunnery seem even more realistic, each time a plane appeared on the screen there were sound effects which made its maneuvers seem very lifelike. In a power dive the plane's engine would snarl and roar with a blast that echoed throughout the whole classroom.

The gunner never knew at which angle the plane would appear on the screen, or whether it would come head on or broadside, or dive, or bank, or veer off before he could train his sights on it.

"This gunnery sure is fun!" Bill Warner exclaimed as their hour's practice came to an end.

"It's just like those shooting galleries where you pay a dime for a round," Bob said.

"It's a darn good method of improving our aim and timing, too," Ted Butler added. "Let's drop over here every evening when we don't have to study or take exams."

"O.K.," Don Allen agreed. "I don't know where else you can get a dime's worth of fun for nothing and, at the same time, learn how to pick off Joe Moto in a Zero!"

MANY A JAP PLANE and landing barge have felt the fatal
sting of the PT boat's .50 caliber machine guns. Every officer
must be an expert gunner.

Grunt and Groan

A chill gray mist was drifting in from the bay as the boys tumbled out of Hut 27 and jogged over to the parade grounds for their daily physical-exercise drill.

"It's a great life if you don't weaken!" Bill Warner exclaimed.

"They certainly weren't kidding when they told us we'd get the works!" Bob replied.

From the very beginning the boys had discovered that what they learned from their manuals, and in their classrooms, was only half the battle if they expected to graduate from Melville as PT boat officers.

Hardened athletes as most of them were, there was scarcely a man among them, that first week, without sore and aching muscles. They knew now what their physical instructor had meant when he looked them over, on the first day, and said, "Well, you fellows look very promising —at least on the surface. But my job is to really toughen you up—and I know my job! Here at Melville we start in where the Commandos leave off!"

Photo by Carroll Van Ark

A GOOD WAY to get over writer's cramp from those weekly exams!

Among the student officers lined up before him, he recognized many who had made names for themselves in the world of sports before coming to the PT Boat Squadrons Training Center. In addition to Ted Butler, All-American tackle, and Don Allen, who had hung up three new track records at Yale, and Bob Reed, outstanding college heavyweight boxer, there were others who had made their mark in various sports.

One was a ski champion who had streaked down Tuckerman's Ravine in record-breaking time just the previous year. Another had played two years of professional football. Three of the boys had been captains of their college elevens, four more were star basketball men, several had been stars on their college swimming and hockey teams, and several others among the new officers were expert boxers.

But as the physical instructor put the boys through their three-quarter-hour period of calisthenics, day after day, they found that training to become PT boat officers brought whole new sets of muscles into play.

But even the physical-exercise drill and the obstacle courses were easy compared with Judo, which was taught them by an iron-muscled man known on the Base as "Butch" Smith. Right after Pearl Harbor, Butch decided that he could serve his country best by giving up his career as a professional wrestler and teaching officers and sailors the art of self-defense. So he joined the Navy, with a Specialist rating, and was promptly sent to Melville.

72

"THE MUSCLE SQUAD" goes into action.

Day after day, in the Base gymnasium, Butch taught small groups of student officers and men the fine points of arm twisting, bone breaking, eye gouging, and other forms of refined murder. He claimed that Judo, as he taught it, was far superior to Japanese jujitsu—and pupils who had had a chance to use it against the Japs in the South Pacific sent back word that he was right!

Bob's first lesson in Judo was an experience he would not soon forget. After half an hour of watching his classmates thumped and pummeled by the instructor, grunting and groaning in body-punishing holds, Bob's turn came. He soon found out that, even with all his boxing experience, he was no match for Butch and his Judo. Crouching low, he tried to draw the instructor out of position by feinting with his right. Then he let go the old "haymaker" that had helped him win his title on the boxing team.

As Bob swung, Butch rolled with the blow and closed in on him before Bob realized what had happened. The next thing he knew, the helpless Ensign was being whirled around and around in the air by the instructor, who had clamped an iron grip on one leg and arm. Then—*thump!*—Bob hit the mat, half dazed.

The instructor bent over him.

"You O.K.?" he asked.

"Sure, I'm all right," Bob answered weakly. "I sort of got the wind knocked out of me, I guess. What happened?"

Patiently the instructor showed Bob his mistakes. They

74

"PARDON ME FOR BREAKING YOUR ARM!" PT
fighters learn the art of Judo.

tried it again. This time Bob was more cautious. But there was little he could do to meet the lightning thrusts and off-balancing tactics of his opponent.

"You're learning," the instructor said by way of encouragement as the lesson ended. "You keep forgetting that *anything* goes in Judo. Don't be afraid of hurting me." He grinned. "I can take it!"

Butch told the boys that next time he would teach them about the correct use of the wicked-looking sheath knife which every PT boatman wears in his belt, along with a .45 automatic, when in combat duty.

"There will be times," he explained, fondling the razor-sharp blade he balanced in his hand, "when this will turn out to be a mighty useful weapon. The Nips are first-rate fighters in a hand-to-hand encounter—but I'll show you a few good tricks to keep up your sleeves."

Very often, as time went on, boxing and wrestling bouts were staged in the Base gymnasium between the divisions which were in training at Melville. Here is the account of Bob Reed's first match as it appeared in *The Skeeter,* the news sheet published at the PT Boat Base each week. Under the headline, "Blow by Blow," the report of the evening's bouts started as follows:

"In the gymnasium last evening a big crowd of officers and men cheered an exhibition of the manly art such as would have warmed the heart of Jack Dempsey himself —to say nothing of winning a contract at Madison Square Garden.

SLUGGING IT OUT on the beach. Many PT boat officers were boxing champs before entering the Navy.

"Sluggers in the first match were Reed vs. Hill—heavyweights. The bout was a free-for-all from start to finish. Both boys came out fast, trading leather in the old one-two ratio. Reed took advantage of a long reach to keep his left in Hill's face. Hill flashed a sockeroo to Reed's chin. Reed landed a solid one on his opponent's jaw. The boys were in a clinch on the ropes at the gong.

"Round Two started fast and furious. Reed landed a left on Hill's nose, which took on a rosy glow. Hill countered with a body blow that rocked Reed on his heels. The round ended in a whirl of leather, both boys still going strong.

"In the third frame of the fracas, Reed connected early with an underslung punch to the button. He followed it with three more head blows. Hill went dead-pan, with that faraway dreamy look in his eye. He missed with a feeble right. Reed closed in for the kill and sent his opponent to the canvas for the count. Winner: Reed, by a knockout."

As a result of his showing that night, Bob found his name posted on the headquarters bulletin board several days later. Along with other men in his division, he had been chosen as a member of the PT Boat Squadrons Training Center boxing squad, which was scheduled for a series of exhibition bouts in Newport the following week. Their opponents, the bulletin announced, would be Coast Guardsmen from the New London base.

ONE DIDN'T MAKE IT—but he will next time! The Navy sees to it that no one gets flabby at Melville.

In the meantime, life at the Base went on much as before—classes, exams, study periods, drills . . . the same stiff routine. Time was growing short, and there were still many things the student officers had to learn before actually getting under way on the Mosquito Boats for the last four weeks of their training.

Photo by Carroll Van Ark

DOWN THE BEACH—the hard way! Future PT boat
Officers take the hurdles on one of the many obstacle courses.

Tin Fish and Ash Cans

Only one week now remained before the student officers were scheduled for "under-way" training. Each day was crammed with activity, from "Reveille" to "Lights Out."

For example, most of one morning was given over to instruction in the use and maintenance of small arms. This was followed by a workout on the rifle range—target practice with both the .45 automatic and the Springfield rifle. Then came a lesson on malfunction—what to do when a rifle or automatic jams or misfires.

Still another period was spent teaching the boys all about the gun turrets and mounts for the .50 caliber machine guns. And in the evening the entire division attended a training movie which taught them how to correct their aim by watching the line of fire made by their tracer bullets.

The future PT boat officers also spent many hours in the torpedo shop, studying the construction and operation of the deadly "tin fish" which every PT boat carries. The instructor first gave them a brief history of the torpedo,

82

A DIVISION OF FUTURE PT OFFICERS marches off to
class past the Quonset huts in which they are quartered.

then told them about today's modern torpedoes—their weight, range, speed, explosive charge, and depth-control mechanism. Some of the torpedoes had been completely torn down so that the boys could see all the separate parts —the war head, engine, propeller shaft, and release mechanism. They were also instructed on how to "ready" a torpedo for firing and how to check the proper angle and lead on their target.

From the torpedo shop the student officers moved on to classroom theory on the use of depth charges, the wicked-looking "ash cans" which a PT boat drops overboard when there are enemy submarines in the near vicinity. Though they were not so complicated as the torpedoes, there was a great deal to learn about regulating the ash cans so that they would explode at the proper depth. There was even a right way and a wrong way to release them from their racks.

Then followed classroom instruction on the smoke-screen generators. The boys were told that although PT boats usually attack in thick weather, or at night, there would be times when they would have to make their own "overcast." By laying a thick smoke screen they could very quickly make themselves an invisible target, even on a clear day. By the time the protective smoke screen lifted, the PT boat's tremendous speed would have carried it beyond the range of the enemy's guns.

Many hours were spent, these last few days, in the

BAD NEWS FOR ENEMY SUBMARINES! Future PT
officers inspect the depth charges—"ash cans"—with which
they may someday destroy lurking subs.

Engineering building. Under the instructor's watchful eye each boy had to show that he knew how to do such things as check the fuel system, from the tankroom to the engines. Aboard one of the boats, alongside the dock, he was shown how to "secure," or shut off, the engines under emergency conditions.

Painstakingly the class was given the inside story of such parts as the superchargers, carburetors, shafts, stern tubes, propellers, rudders, exhaust stacks, and manifolds. The instructor drilled them on the various parts of the engines which must be checked at regular intervals. Some parts had to be checked every twenty-five hours; others, every fifty hours; and still others, every one hundred hours.

The boys were also taught how to operate and care for the auxiliary generator, which was used to supply current for lights, stove, and power whenever the boat was not under way. When under way, of course, power was supplied by the main generators of the engines.

The young officers learned, too, how to keep the engine-room log, which must be turned in daily to the Squadron Engineer.

The grand climax of their engineering training was a complete teardown and reassembly of a Packard PT boat supermarine engine.

Finally the last week of solid classroom theory and instruction came to an end. True, there would still be classes to attend—right up until the time the student officers

Photo by Carroll Van Ark

THREE PT SAILORS learn the fine points of adjusting and putting on their gas masks.

graduated from Melville. But, from now on, much of their time would be spent under way, on PT boats. Starting on the following day, they would no longer be mere land-lubbers!

Under Way

There was a heavy overcast, with a slight drizzle of rain, as the student officers gathered on the dock for their first day under way.

"A swell day for a picnic—indoors!" Bob Reed remarked, looking out over the gray bay.

"At least it's calm on the briny deep," Bill Warner said.

Three of the PT boats were already warming up. Their regular officers and crews were aboard, making the customary preparations for under-way operation. One of the boats was Number 176, on which the boys had been out during their first week at Melville. The other two were numbered 180 and 182.

This morning, as always, the deep-throated rumble of the idling PT boat engines gave Bob Reed a tremendous thrill. He experienced the same wave of excitement he had felt on his first visit to an airport, years ago, as a small boy. But the powerful blast of the air liner's twin motors, warming up for the take-off, couldn't begin to compare with the throbbing of a PT boat's trio of 12 cylinder Packard power plants. These brute engines spoke a two-word language all their own: Power and Speed! More power and speed than had ever before been packed into a boat only eighty feet long!

Now Lieutenant (j.g.) Tom Moran, the skipper of PT Boat 176, was motioning for the boys to come aboard. The division, split up into three groups, boarded the three PT boats. Bob Reed, Bill Warner, and Don Allen were in the group that went aboard PT 176.

"We are going out now on torpedo practice," Lieutenant Moran explained as the student officers gathered around him in the cockpit, adjusting their kapok life jackets. And he described the maneuvers they would carry out. "When we get out in the bay," he continued, "one PT boat will pretend that it is the target. It will hold a steady course at about seven knots, which is about the way a slow tanker would travel. The other two boats will deploy, then rush in for the attack."

The Executive Officer interrupted at this point to explain that on today's practice runs they would not actually fire torpedoes.

"That's right," the skipper said. "I'll give you the pitch on the whole thing very briefly. One of you will take over as skipper. Another will act as torpedoman, sighting the target and directing the helmsman on the correct approach. When we come within effective torpedo range, the skipper will give the order to fire. At that instant the man at the wheel, instead of pressing the button which would release one of the torpedoes, shall simply throttle down to

90

the exact speed at which a torpedo travels through the water, and hold the exact torpedo course.

"Thus, for all practical purposes, our PT boat becomes the torpedo itself. If the course of our boat intersects the course of the target boat, that means we would have scored a hit if we had actually fired a torpedo. Does everyone get it? O.K. We'll get under way. On the first run our boat will be the target—on a five-mile course down the middle of the bay."

PT Boats 180 and 182 had already nudged out from their docks and were headed out into the bay. Seamen on the dock alongside PT 176 cast off the lines. The sailors aboard hauled in the lines and fenders. The skipper moved his three throttles forward and the boat leaped ahead through the water, swinging in a wide arc out through the lagoon.

Traveling at about thirty-five knots, it took only a few minutes for the boat to reach a point in the bay midway between the two shores. The skipper came about on a southerly course, throttling his engines down as far as they would go. In the distance, along the shore to starboard, the boys could see PT 180 hovering outside a small cove, waiting to attack them. PT 182 was streaking down the bay past the opposite shore, deploying to come in for the attack from the other direction.

Lieutenant Moran turned to Bill Warner, who happened to be standing next to him.

"Take the helm and hold this course, down the middle

of the bay," he said. "Watch your r.p.m. gauge and give her just enough throttle to hold her at seven knots. From now on we're a tanker."

Bill took over the wheel and carefully adjusted his throttles to hold the PT boat at the required low speed. Now they were barely crawling along, the three screws stirring up a gentle gurgling wake.

In a few minutes the boys could see PT 180 veering out from shore toward them. From the white "rooster tail" she was tossing up, they could tell that she was cutting through the water at a good clip.

"Looks as though they might get us," Bob commented.

"I'm not so sure," Lieutenant Moran replied. "He's circling out now to allow more lead on his target—but I think he underestimated the distance to begin with and it's too late to make it up."

When the attacking boat was still a good many hundred yards away, they could tell that the skipper had probably given the order to fire; for PT 180 straightened out on a course directly toward them and slowed down to the speed at which a torpedo travels through the water.

On she came, closer and closer. But Lieutenant Moran had guessed correctly. The skipper of PT 180 had not estimated the target's speed and distance accurately. The "tanker," PT 176, moved across the bow of the incoming boat with plenty of water between them.

"That was a miss," Lieutenant Moran said as PT 180 swept past, astern, at about thirty knots. "Hold your

Photo by Carroll Van Ark

"TARGET DEAD AHEAD!" One Ensign takes the helm while
his companion mans the torpedo director.

course—here comes PT 182!" he directed the helmsman. "Looks as if he'd figured out his range and angle a little better than the first boat did."

The attacker was streaking across the bay toward them, on an oblique course, about three-quarters head on. Now it had "fired its torpedo" and was holding a fixed course, speeding on toward its sluggish target.

For several anxious moments, as PT 182 came in closer and closer, Bill Warner knew how the captain of a real tanker must feel when he sees a torpedo speeding toward him—a deadly tin fish from which his slow-moving ship cannot possibly escape.

On it came, knifing the water, straight at the target! At the last minute, just when a collision seemed unavoidable, PT 182 swerved to starboard and swept by, banking huge rollers against the hull of PT 176. Some of the crew were cheering and waving as the boats passed, a scant ten feet apart!

"That would have been a perfect hit," Lieutenant Moran said. "He timed his run beautifully. Now it's our turn. Let's see if we can do as well."

He took over the helm from Bill Warner and advanced the throttles. The engines thundered at 2500 r.p.m.'s and the boat plunged forward, as though eager to show its skipper that a streamlined torpedo boat capable of express-train speed should never have to slog along at a tanker's seven knots, even in torpedo practice!

By this time the drizzle had increased to rain, which stung

94

the faces of the PT boat officers like sleet as they flew along over the surface of the bay. The bridge of a PT boat is not a closed cabin. It is an open cockpit which affords no protection to the faces of the men who stand in it.

"There will be poor visibility on this run," the skipper said in a loud voice that could be heard above the roar of the engines. "Ideal attack conditions," he added, giving the boat a little left rudder to bring it over along the east shore into a bank of low-hanging mist. Picking a protected spot behind a point of land, he swung the boat around and retarded his throttles. Then he motioned to Bob Reed.

"You will take over as skipper for the attack, Reed," he announced. "Allen, you will act as torpedoman."

While the others grouped themselves around him as closely as they could, he explained to Don the method of using the torpedo director, which was mounted on the forward edge of the instrument panel on the starboard side of the cockpit.

The torpedo director worked on very much the same principle as a gun sight, but it was not quite so simple. Lieutenant Moran showed Don how to sight his target through the torpedo director, and then how to use it in order to estimate the speed and course of the target. He told Don that as soon as he sighted the target it would be his job to give steering directions to the helmsman, so that the boat would follow a course which would result in the correct angle of torpedo fire—much the same way that a bombardier in a bombing plane gives directions to

95

the pilot for the run onto the target. Thus for a few action-filled minutes the director-operator becomes the commander of the PT boat.

The skipper raised his binoculars and scanned the bay.

"The target boat has started," he said, handing the glasses to Bob.

Bob trained them on the section of the bay which the skipper had indicated.

"I can't see her," he said, squinting to keep the rain out of his eyes.

"Well, she's there—bearing down on us," Lieutenant Moran insisted. "You've got to train yourself to see your target under conditions like this. You're just kidding yourself if you think that a Jap warship is going to be obliging enough to stand out in a sharp silhouette against a blue sky, just so you can smack a fish into her. It just never happens that way, Reed. When you get out on combat duty you'll find that you've got to hunt 'em out in weather like this, and worse—then rush in, fire your torpedo, and get out again."

Bob peered through the rain again—and picked up his target. Advancing his throttles, he started his run, skimming up the bay at about forty-five knots and standing slightly offshore to take advantage of the protective mist that was hugging the land.

Don Allen hunched over his torpedo director. He had to wipe off his binoculars with lens paper almost constantly because of the rain. Now the "tanker" target could

SKIDDING INTO A TIGHT "U" TURN, a PT boat
streaks away from the target boat. Score: a sure hit!

be seen quite clearly, even without glasses. PT 180 was slogging down the middle of the bay so close now that Don was able to calibrate her speed on the director.

Still squinting along the sight, he joggled his left hand as a signal to Bob to bring PT 176 on an oblique course for the target run.

"Left rudder—left," he called out. "Now a little more."

The executive officer, standing beside Don, cautioned him to give his orders to the helmsman more clearly.

"Snap out your orders in a distinct, seamanlike manner so they can be heard, Allen!" he said. "This isn't a guessing game between you and the skipper. Tell him what you want—and don't make him strain to hear what you're saying!"

The target was in clear focus through the director. Don raised his hand once more.

"A little to the right—*right!*" he barked out.

Bob turned the wheel slightly, as directed, tensely watching the "tanker" on which they were bearing down at such terrific speed.

As they swept in for the kill, Don raised his left hand to attract Bob's attention.

Then, peering intently through the torpedo director, he shouted, "Stand by to fire!"

Bob reached for his throttle knobs, ready to move them back the instant the order came.

Suddenly Don dropped his arm and snapped out the order, *"Fire!"*

98

Bob instantly throttled down to exact torpedo speed and, with a firm grip on the wheel, concentrated on holding the boat on its arrowlike course toward the target. For, according to the rules of the game, PT 176 was now the torpedo itself.

Every man in the cockpit was tense as the boat sped on toward its helpless target. Grasping the handrails tightly, and leaning forward against the force of the wind, they waited anxiously to see whether this run would score a hit or a miss.

Now the "tanker" was so close that they could see the faces of the men aboard her.

"Looks like a hit, all right," Lieutenant Moran said. "I'll take over now, Reed," and he moved in behind the wheel.

Now only a distance of a hundred feet separated the "torpedo" from its target. Now seventy-five feet. Now fifty! The student officers braced themselves instinctively for the crash that was about to take place.

But, at the last split second, the skipper grabbed the speed knob on the wheel and, pushing his throttle to "Full ahead," whirled PT 176 about in a sharp skidding turn that cleared the target only by a cat's whisker! The mighty engines in the hull responded magnificently, roaring their defiance and churning up a boiling white plume as PT 176 streaked into its getaway maneuver. The boys cheered and waved to their classmates on the "tanker," now wallowing and bucking like a bronco in the swell of their wake.

99

Lieutenant Moran straightened out on his course for the run up the bay, to deploy into position for the next attack—this time, on PT 182.

"Nice work, men!" he called out above the roar of the engines. "That was a perfect hit!"

Bob Reed and Don Allen moved toward the rear of the cockpit so that the next two men could take their places as skipper and helmsman. Their faces were red from the wind and wet with rain.

"You were really cooking on that run, skipper!" Don grinned. "We were right on the old beam!"

"You were the guy who did it, Don," Bob said. "I was just the chauffeur."

"Remember what the C.O. told us about teamwork when we first came to Melville? I guess he was right. Fighting a PT is no one-man job!" Don reminded him. "If we do as well when we're really mixing it up with the Axis, we'll be able to paint a rising sun or a swastika insigne on our cockpit for a hit like the one we just made."

"That will be the day!" Bob exclaimed.

And he tightened his grip on the handrail as PT 176 skidded into an S curve for the next attack.

ROOSTER PLUME—a PT boat, turning at full throttle, is
almost hidden by the spray churned up by its screws.

Gremlins

One evening the officers and men gathered in the auditorium for an informal talk by the Commanding Officer of the Base.

"What's the Old Man shooting the breeze about to-night?" Bill Warner asked as the boys from Hut 27 walked over to the hall.

"The scuttle butt is that he's going to spring some new Base rules on us," Bob replied.

"That's not the way I heard it," Don Allen said. "The C.O. is plenty burned up about those two men in Hut 98 who washed out last week. My guess is that he's going to lay down the law to the rest of us."

But when all the officers and men were seated and the Lieutenant Commander rose to speak, it was clear that he was in a jovial mood.

"Now that all of you have been under way on MTB's, I have some friendly advice I'd like to pass along," he commenced. "In short, I would like to tell you something about PT boat Gremlins. Perhaps some of you think that aviators are the only people who have to deal with Gremlins; but if you do, you're wrong. Any old-time **PT** boat-man will agree with me, I'm sure.

"For the benefit of any new men who have not yet run up against our special breed of Gremlins, I'd like to describe them to you," he continued, with a twinkle. "Our **PT** boat Gremlins are quite small, about the size of a Brownie. They wear tights, bobtailed frock coats, and long pointed shoes. They live in the bilges of the boat and, although they are usually pretty quiet in smooth water, you'll often see them snooping around with their long pointed noses, just itching to make trouble, the minute you get into rough water."

The C.O. then told about one of the more common **PT** boat Gremlins. This pesky little rascal loves rough water —especially on a day when the salt spray keeps flying into the skipper's face, so that he has to wipe his face and binoculars almost constantly. Then, just as the skipper raises his glasses once again to take a look at some suspicious object in the distance, the Gremlin sneaks up and heaves a bucket of salt water which catches the skipper full in the face.

"You won't be able to see the Gremlin or his bucket," the C.O. added, "but you'll know they are there. And by the time you have cleared your face and glasses again, the object you wanted to see has completely disappeared."

The boys laughed at his description of this well-known **PT** boat Gremlin, for many of them had often put up with his antics.

"This particular Gremlin has a cousin," the C.O. went on. "You'll meet him someday when you've been ducking down behind the bridge windshield every time the crest of a cold green eight-foot wave breaks over the cockpit. Suddenly, as you duck down for the fiftieth time, this little Gremlin jabs a needle into you, so that you pop up just in time to catch the full force of the next wave right in your face."

Another Gremlin, he explained, was very fond of depth charges. His favorite trick was to wait until a PT boat was coming in from an all-night patrol. As soon as the boat got well inside, where the channel was about twenty-nine feet deep, this Gremlin would come up out of the bilges and watch the torpedoman checking the release and setting each ash can back on "Safe." As soon as the torpedoman turned his back, the Gremlin would slyly kick one of the ash cans overboard—after setting the index pointer so that it would explode at thirty feet!

The story of that Gremlin brought a laugh from the audience. But there wasn't a man in the hall who didn't almost shudder when he thought of the danger of trying to raise an unexploded depth charge, set to go off at thirty feet, in a harbor channel only twenty-nine feet deep! The C.O. paused to let his tale of the ash-can Gremlin sink in a bit.

"I just happened to think of another Gremlin who is quite a troublemaker, too," he continued. "In fact, I think one of the men in this room learned about this Gremlin

104

"ACK-ACK" in the making. Future PT Skippers learn the inside story of their .50 caliber machine guns.

just the other day." The Commanding Officer's glance swept the room. "Well, I don't see the man I'm talking about. Anyhow, he finally got a breathing spell last Saturday and was looking forward to spending some of his forty-eight-hour leave with a certain person—a *very* certain person!" he added, with a smile. "Boat inspection had been scheduled for Saturday morning, and he had gone over his PT boat compartment and it looked mighty shipshape—good for at least a 3.89. However, when the inspecting officer went aboard and just for luck pulled up a floor board, what do you suppose that Gremlin had done? He had thrown a dirty dungaree jacket into the bilges right where the Commander could see it—a jacket which the gunner's mate said he had lost three weeks before. So, instead of being able to keep his date, the PT boatman spent a dull week end on the Base, as a penalty.

"That just shows you can't trust a Gremlin, especially when you have a leave coming up!" the C.O. chuckled. "I only hope that the cute little friend of the gunner's mate understands all about PT boat Gremlins."

He then went on to tell the boys that sometimes the Gremlins have been known to leave the PT boats and come ashore to cause mischief around the Base.

"They don't do this very often," he admitted, "because they have trouble getting their shore legs and they don't walk very steadily. And after they've been ashore it's hard for them to get their sea legs back again."

But in rare cases, he explained, they have waddled

ashore, and they seemed to have an especial fondness for the kerosene stoves which warm the Quonset huts. Sometimes they turn the stoves way up, trying to smoke out the men who live in the hut. At other times, when the wind shifts to the north and whips up a gale with the thermometer down almost to zero, the Gremlins put on their ear muffs and come ashore to turn off as many stoves as they can find, before they are discovered.

"And there's one impish little Gremlin," the C.O. added, "who sometimes comes ashore and flicks on the lights after taps, just as the Duty Officer is making his rounds."

He told of still another of the little wretches who once tagged along behind an officer who was on overnight leave up in Boston. As soon as the officer fell sound asleep the Gremlin shut off his alarm clock, which had been set for an early hour. Result: the officer overslept, failed to get back to the Base on time, and received a severe penalty for overstaying his leave.

"They're a wicked little people, these PT boat Gremlins," the Commanding Officer concluded. "You'll find them making your dots into dashes when you're trying to flash an identification signal . . . and they will sometimes short-circuit your compass light at night, and you will suddenly discover that you have been steering three-zero-magnetic when you should have been steering three-double-zero. Other times you will be out on patrol and you'll slip down into the galley for a mug of hot Joe and a sandwich—and there won't be any. Then you'll discover that it was payday for the Gremlins. They had a party in the galley, ate all the sandwiches, and threw the Joe overboard."

This was one of the saddest pranks a Gremlin could possibly play. For every Navy man loves his Joe—his cup of hot coffee—every hour or so, especially when he is under way.

The Commanding Officer related still other misdeeds of the PT boat Gremlins—many of them being military secrets which even a Gremlin wasn't supposed to know. Sometimes they would short-circuit the torpedo-firing mechanism, and when the skipper pushed the button to fire his torpedo nothing would happen. Some of the Gremlins loved to crawl inside the .50 caliber machine guns and foul up the mechanism, so they would jam or misfire. Others liked to monkey with the torpedo director, so that a sure hit would turn out to be a miserable miss. And so it went.

Finally the C.O. brought his talk to an end. "Watch out for the Gremlins, lads," he cautioned them. "If they haven't entered your life yet, they will soon—and they will cause you trouble as long as you sail with an MTB Squadron. So—watch out for them!"

As the boys filed out of the auditorium and walked back to their quarters, they realized that the C.O. had talked about the Gremlins merely as a way of giving them some sound advice which every PT boatman should keep in

Photo by Carroll Van Ark

ENLISTED MEN line up for inspection.

mind. Although it had been a very amusing talk, they knew that its chief purpose had been to warn them—not to amuse them.

Sometimes, they knew, it was very convenient to blame Gremlins for things that happened because a man himself was careless. "Being on the watch for Gremlins" simply meant being constantly on the alert to prevent accidents or other mishaps due to carelessness.

Ack-ack

As Ensign Bob Reed and his classmates swung into the final weeks of their training at the MTB Base, the routine was stepped up to a fast and furious pace.

Only two men in the class had washed out, thus far. They had taken extra periods of work to make up their low marks, but the course was too stiff for them.

For all the student officers there was still the weekly series of exams and tests. Each boy knew that he must keep up with his daily work, or he would fall hopelessly behind and flunk his exam.

The toughest exams, of course, would be the final ones at the end of the training.

But the Senior Instructor warned the boys one day, as they were taking their regular week-end exam, "*Any* exam can be the final exam for the man who fails to get a passing mark. Unless he gets at least 3.00, he's through."

Perhaps the most important tests of all were the two aptitude tests which every boy had to pass. One was given midway through the course. The other one was given just before the final exams.

In the aptitude test each boy was carefully checked on a long list of questions which showed his qualifications as a PT boat officer. Some of the questions were about the subjects studied in the classrooms. Others were designed to show how fast a boy could think in case of a sudden emergency, or how he would meet a certain unexpected situation if he were commanding his own boat. Other questions were tests of his knowledge of Seamanship and Navigation, Communications, Engineering, and Gunnery.

Bob Reed passed his first aptitude test with flying colors —an average mark of 3.75. On many of the questions he pulled down the perfect mark—4.00. But on Navigation he muffed a couple of important equations—for a 2.80. He was able to make up this shortcoming, however, by putting in three evenings of extra-period work.

Part of each man's training was the task of inspecting the quarters of the enlisted men—just as their own quarters, in turn, were regularly inspected by their senior officers. When inspecting the enlisted men's quarters, the student officers learned how to give necessary orders in such a way as to command authority and respect.

Sometimes, if a seaman failed to perform his duties correctly, it was necessary to "restrict" him. This meant that his week-end liberty was canceled and that he must remain on the Base. The student officers did not like to restrict an enlisted man, even when he deserved it. But it was their duty to do so. In fact, they themselves were sometimes restricted by their senior officers. It was all

Photo by Carroll Van Ark

"NOW HEAR THIS!" blares the Training Center loud-speaker.
This Ensign is wanted at the Personnel Office.

part of being in the Navy, where discipline and respect to officers are all-important.

Bob Reed had occasion to be reminded of this fact one morning when he stopped by to see the Duty Officer on a routine matter, on his way to the docks for machine-gun practice. As he was filling out the form which the O.D. had given him, two sailors came in. They walked up to the Duty Officer's desk, and one of the seamen said, "I'd like to request shore leave today. I have a stand-by."

There was nothing unusual in such a request. A man could sometimes have a day of liberty, even though it was not yet his turn, provided some other man agreed to stand by and take over his duties.

Bob thought it rather strange, however, that the sailor had failed to address his officer as "Sir." From the black look on the O.D.'s face he judged that the fireworks were about to start.

"What's your name?" the Duty Officer asked.

"Jones," came the reply.

"Jones *What!*" snapped the officer, whose face was now growing red.

"S. D. Jones, Seaman, third class," came the mumbled reply.

By this time the Duty Officer could scarcely contain himself.

He said, "Don't you know you're supposed to say *'Sir'* when you address an officer?"

"Yes, sir," the seaman replied meekly.

114

"Where did you get your boot training?" the O.D. asked.

"Norfolk," the boy answered.

"*Sir!*" the O.D. prompted him once again. The second sailor stood fumbling his hat, embarrassed that his shipmate could be so completely stupid. The O.D. glared at the first sailor. Finally he said, "Request for liberty denied. That's all," and turned back to the papers on his desk, wagging his head sadly. As the two sailors left, he exclaimed to himself in disgust, "When they're as dumb as that, why do they always have to pick the Navy!"

Bob tiptoed out and hurried down to the docks so as not to be late for gunnery practice. When he got there, the other student officers were already boarding the boats. Lieutenant Moran, the skipper of PT 176, motioned to him to hurry. As soon as Bob had clambered aboard, the three boats got under way.

His arriving just at the last minute reminded him of an incident that had happened the week before. A seaman, scheduled for his first PT boat cruise, ran down to the docks pell-mell to board his boat. He wasn't certain of the number of the boat he was supposed to go out on. He thought it was PT 65.

Sure enough, when he got to the docks, there was PT 65, engines turning over slowly, about twenty-five feet off the dock. In his eagerness not to be restricted for arriving late, he plunged into the water and struck out for the PT boat. As he swam up alongside, one of the sailors reached over and fished him out of the lagoon.

"What's the matter, gob?" he asked. "We'd have been alongside the dock in another minute or two. Couldn't you wait?"

Puffing and spluttering, the seaman replied, "But I thought you were going out, and I didn't want to be left behind."

The sailor roared with laughter.

"You're supposed to be on PT 56, I guess. She's getting ready to go out now. *We're coming in!*"

For under-way gunnery practice the PT boat always went outside the bay into open water. Lieutenant Moran explained to the boys just what they would have to do. When the three PT's got outside, he said, they would cruise up and down, three abreast, each boat several hundred yards apart. A Navy plane would fly over them, at right angles, towing a sleeve target. One man in each PT would fire at the moving target from the gun turret as it passed over his boat. The fire must always be directed seaward, the skipper added, so that stray fifties would be certain not to hit anyone on land, but would spend themselves and fall into the ocean.

The three PT's—176, 180, and 182—streaked down the bay in column formation, led by PT 180. PT 176 was in second place, riding the smooth ribbon of wake which the leading boat laid down like a highway.

The bay was as calm as a millpond. When the boats

A GUNNER'S MATE mans the tail-stinger of a PT boat.
The deadly Oerlikon gun is bad medicine for enemy planes.

reached open water, there was a slight swell which they rode easily. It was really a perfect day for gunnery practice.

PT 180, in the lead, throttled down and swung onto a westerly course. The other two boats fanned out and came about in an "on the beam" formation. Now they were running abreast, at about ten knots.

Under the direction of the gunner's mate, two of the Ensigns on PT 176 were readying the starboard turret for firing. One of them mounted a loaded drum of .50 caliber bullets so that they would feed into the chamber. Another boy took his position in the turret as gunner.

The gunner's mate cautioned him not to fire until he gave the order.

"Remember everything you've learned about leading a moving target," he reminded the Ensign. "But don't lead it too much. The pilot of that tow plane is a grand guy and he enjoys living. He's not too keen on being shot down by a green PT boat gunner."

Now they could see the Navy target plane, a mere speck to the north, off their port side. On it came, growing larger as it neared them. Finally the sleeve target could be clearly seen against the gray sky, trailing far behind the plane.

The gunner of the first boat in the formation was now training his machine guns on the approaching target.

In another instant the gunner's mate on PT 176 barked out, "Stand by to fire!"

The boy in the turret swung his machine guns toward

"STAND BY TO FIRE!"—A young PT Officer mans the antiaircraft guns as the sleeve target comes within range.

the oncoming plane. He had the sleeve in his sights.

PT 180 was the first to let go as the target passed overhead. The staccato clatter of the guns shattered the air and a stream of tracer bullets skyrocketed upward toward the target.

In a second the plane was over PT 176. The gunner's mate held his hand poised in mid-air. He swung it downward and gave the order *"Fire!"* The boy in the turret opened up with both barrels as the sleeve target slipped through the sky over his head. The roar of the ack-ack was deafening. Empty shells spewed out of the magazines and cascaded onto the deck. The tracers sped upward in a swift arc. Some of the bullets could be seen ripping through the cloth of the target. But most of them fell short, trailing the target. In a flash it was all over. The guns were silent again.

Several seconds later the plane passed over the third boat in the formation, PT 182. Her gunner opened fire. The plane then passed on, out to sea, while the three PT's swung about to double back on their course.

Now the plane was banking in the distance. It was turning to come about for another target run over the three Mosquito Boats.

"All right," the gunner's mate said briskly. "Man the port turret," and he motioned to Bill Warner, who slipped a loaded drum of ammunition into place. "Reed, man the guns!" the petty officer barked.

Bob took his place at the brace of machine guns.

120

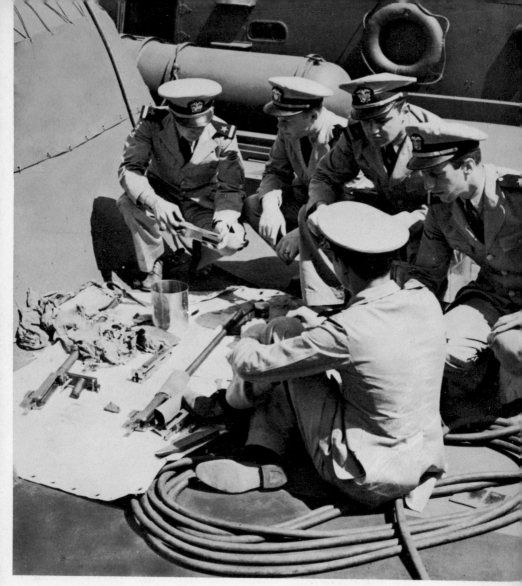

"TAKE 'EM APART—PUT 'EM TOGETHER!" Every PT
Officer must know how to repair a machine gun under service conditions.

The plane was holding a beeline course toward them and coming in fast. Bob cast a hurried glance to starboard at PT 182, which would have the first crack at the target on this run. Her gunner was swinging his antiaircraft guns into position. Now he was giving the target a burst —and on it came!

The gunner's mate on PT 176 gave the order "Stand by to fire!" Bob trained his ring sights on the speeding aerial target. Closer and closer it came. The plane thundered by overhead. Now . . . *"Fire!"* came the order. Bob braced himself in the turret and squeezed the twin triggers. The ack-ack tracers made a continuous trail of red-hot lead that ripped through the target as it streaked by. Now it was gone. Bob relaxed his grip on the guns and looked over at PT 180, whose gunner was now giving the target the works.

This was exciting stuff! The only trouble was it was almost over before you could really draw a bead on the 200 m.p.h. target. But it was for these few seconds of concentrated action that a gunner must spend hours in a classroom, more hours poring over his manuals, and more hours out on actual gunnery practice. Anybody could shoot ack-ack up into the sky, but it took a good man, with plenty of savvy, to really hit the speeding target.

Now the three PT's were completing their easterly run and were falling back into "on the beam" formation for the next target run.

"Someday soon," Bob thought to himself, "that

friendly U. S. Navy plane with its sleeve target will be a Jap Zero dive bomber with the hateful rising sun insignia on its wings."

And he watched carefully as his classmates each took their turn in the antiaircraft turrets, for he knew that a man can often improve his own performance by watching the good work, as well as the mistakes, of others.

He realized that this was an important part of the team-work training of MTB personnel. Each officer must be a good gunner, as well as an efficient PT boat commander. For he never knew when his gunner might get knocked out in action—and then his own skill as a gunner might well be the means of saving the rest of the crew and the boat itself.

"Torpedo's Away!"

When Bob Reed went to the officers' mess the following noon, he saw a group of his classmates in front of the bulletin board. Whatever they were reading seemed to be very funny, for they were all chuckling.

"Hey, Bob, come on over and get a load of this," Bill Warner called.

"What's up?" Bob asked as he joined them.

"The Skipper has been preaching Safety First so much that now he's trying it in verse," Ted Butler explained. "Read that first one. When he wrote it, he was probably thinking of that ex-PT that's pulled up on the quay with its hull stove in."

Bob read the verse, which went like this:

Toot the flute, loud and long, for Ensign Joseph Lode,
A PT skipper who seldom followed the rules of the road.

"Here's a good one, too," Bill Warner said, pointing to the next verse. "Lookit . . ."

Toll the bell for Machinist's Mate McBrawn,
Who started the engines with the mufflers on.

124

"Wow! He probably got enough back pressure in his manifolds to blow him up through the topside!" Bob exclaimed. "Here's one you should have known about yesterday, Bill, when the gunner's mate bawled you out for the way you were handling the guns."

Muffle the drum for Gunner's Mate McSnifty,
Who looked down the muzzle of a loaded fifty.

Still another verse kidded the awkward seaman who did everything wrong when mooring an MTB at the dock. It went:

A silent prayer for Seaman Oscar Block,
Who used legs, arms, and body to fend her off the dock.

Another was a warning to the careless engineer.

A small brass plaque for Engineer McLean,
He lit a match to see if his gas filters were clean.

The last one was about a mistake which was sometimes made by absent-minded torpedomen.

Bow your heads for Torpedoman John,
Who fired his fish with the propeller locks on.

"Those are all right," Bob remarked. "And here's another one I just made up myself. I'm no piker when it comes to writing poems. Maybe they're not much good, but at least they're four-liners."

The lads in Château 27
Will never get to PT heaven
If they don't start to scurry
Down to the docks in a hurry!"

125

"Gee, that's corny!" exclaimed Don Allen. "But you're right, Bob," he added, glancing at his wrist watch. "It's 1255 now, and we're due for torpedo practice at 1300. Come on!"

The young Ensigns went down to the lagoon on the double, stopping off just long enough at Hut 27 to pick up their under-way gear. Separating into two groups, they clambered aboard PT 148 and 150 just as the seamen were casting off the lines.

Bob Reed and Bill Warner found themselves together on PT 150. The skipper, Lieutenant Ed Graham, greeted them cordially.

"Welcome aboard, men," he said. Then, turning to Bob, he added, "That was a good fight you put on up in Newport the other night, Reed. I thought that Coast Guardsman had you in the first round—until you connected with the old PT roundhouse swing on the button."

"Thanks, Lieutenant," Bob replied. "I thought he had me, too. They sure grow 'em tough up in New London."

"Yeah, but they're tougher here at Melville, hey?" The skipper grinned.

As the torpedo boat got under way and sped out through the lagoon into the bay, Lieutenant Graham explained the maneuvers they would carry out that afternoon.

"Today, for the first time, you will be firing real torpedoes," he told the boys. "The target is the small motorboat you see dead ahead, out in the bay. It will follow a

126

A MOSQUITO BOAT'S BIG STING—unusual view looking along
the port torpedo tubes of a PT boat.

fixed course, while we come in on an angle for the attack. The procedure is very much the same as that which you followed the other day when you were out with Lieutenant Moran."

He went on to explain that the torpedoes they would fire were known as "exercise" torpedoes. They were like real torpedoes in every way except for the fact that their explosive war heads had been removed. In place of the war head there was a harmless dummy head, or "practice" head, which would not explode on contact.

"Real torpedoes cost a good many thousand dollars apiece," the executive officer remarked. "They are rather expensive toys to play with, even if we didn't mind blowing up the personnel on the target boat."

The skipper told the student officers that the torpedoes for today's practice had been set at a sufficient depth to pass safely under the target. Otherwise, even a dummy torpedo would crash through the thin wooden hull of a small boat, because it traveled at such terrific speed.

"And when the torpedo finally comes up to the surface again on the other side of the target," he added, "the Base launch goes out and retrieves it and tows it back to port."

By this time PT 148 was beating down the bay along the opposite shore, traveling at almost full throttle. PT 150 followed the near shore and had long since outdistanced the plodding target boat. The Base launch hovered in the distance, far astern of the target.

"Reed, you will take the helm on the first run," the

Photo by Carroll Van Ark

A TENSE MOMENT—the torpedoman stands by, ready to whack the percussion head with his mallet in case the firing circuit goes haywire.

skipper announced as he throttled down. "Warner, how's your eye today? Try your luck at the torpedo director, as torpedoman."

The boys took their posts. The other Ensigns crowded in as close as they could, in order to watch every move their two classmates made.

"All right," Lieutenant Graham said, "ease her out toward the target while Warner calibrates the target's speed and estimates his firing angle. And don't forget— throttle down for a minute the instant the torpedo is fired. Then give her the gun for the getaway. Otherwise you'll run over your own torpedo, and I don't want to be around when *that* happens!"

Bob moved his throttles forward, stepping up his r.p.m.'s until the three Packard engines were driving the MTB along at about twenty knots.

Bill adjusted his torpedo director, drawing a bead on the slow-moving motorboat which was their target.

"What do you get?" Lieutenant Graham inquired.

"I think she's traveling at ten knots—maybe twelve," Bill replied, peering through his torpedo director for a final checkup.

"That's about right," the skipper said. "She's supposed to do twelve, but she's bucking a slight head wind. All right, fellows—from here on it's your show. Make it good!"

At a signal from his torpedoman Bob stepped up his speed to approximately forty-five knots, to rush in for the attack. He was tense with excitement as he realized

"TORPEDO'S AWAY!"—a fish hurtles from its tube and
streaks toward the target.

that this maneuver would be close to the real thing, just as they would do it in actual combat.

Bill asked for more right rudder, to compensate for the speed at which they were traveling. Bob turned the wheel, changing their course a couple of points.

"Hold it! That's right on the beam!" Bill called out.

Now they were bearing down headlong onto the target boat. Bill, making a slight adjustment in his torpedo director, raised his left hand and held it in mid-air as a signal that it was almost time to let go.

"Stand by to fire!" he sang out.

Closer and closer the target loomed up ahead of them. Bob took his left hand off the wheel and held it poised over the electric button which would send Torpedo Number 1 crashing on its fatal mission.

Now, surely, it was time to let go, he thought. But still the order hadn't come. Then it happened!

Bill jerked his hand downward and shouted, *"Fire!"*

Bob pressed the torpedo button and, with a roar that shattered the air, the torpedo shot out of Tube Number 1 and hurtled through the air into the water.

"Torpedo's away!" cried the torpedoman.

Quickly Bob pulled back his three throttle knobs in order not to overrun his torpedo.

Then he jammed them full open. Giving PT 150 hard right rudder, he shot the torpedo boat away from that spot like a scared rabbit. The three screws kicked up a "rooster tail" that looked like a waterfall in reverse!

132

Bob looked back through the spray which broke over the bridge windshield and saw the thin telltale wake made by the propeller of the fish as it sizzled through the water in a beeline toward its target. Lieutenant Graham raised his binoculars and trained them on the torpedo's wake as it intercepted the course of the target boat.

"It's a hit!" he exclaimed, shouting to make himself heard. "It went directly under the boat, amidships."

Bob grinned at his torpedoman, and Bill grinned back. Then he skidded the PT into an S turn and throttled down, about half a mile astern of the target boat.

"Feeling pretty cocky, aren't you!" Lieutenant Graham commented dryly as he took over the helm. "Well, I wouldn't if I were you. One lucky hit doesn't make you Lieutenant Commander Bulkeley, you know."

But his remark was more good-natured kidding than sarcasm. He could still remember the thrill of *his* first torpedo hit when he had been in training as an Ensign, not so long ago.

"On the next run," he said, "you two men swap places. Warner at the helm, Reed as torpedoman. All right, supermen—take over," he added jokingly.

As Bill turned the PT for the leisurely trip back toward the shore for the next attack, they could see their sister ship rushing in on the target boat, several miles ahead. Then she fired her torpedo. Off to starboard was the Base launch, making its way over to the spot where the spent torpedo would probably come to the surface.

133

Night Attack

The period of training was now rapidly drawing to an end for Ensign Bob Reed and the student officers and enlisted men who had come to Melville almost two months ago.

More and more, the officers and men were being welded together into smooth-working fighting teams as they polished up on the fine points of their Gunnery, Boat Handling, Navigation, Torpedo Work, Engineering, and Communications.

The regular squadron skippers were beginning to find out which men were best at certain jobs. For example, one of the seamen who shipped as a cook was found to be a first-rate torpedoman. He was better than most of the regular torpedomen at using the "seaman's eye" method of estimating the speed of the target and angle of attack. And one of the new officers was a whiz at handling the deadly Oerlikon gun. There wasn't a gunner's mate in the entire squadron who could lead a flying-sleeve target more accurately or score more hits.

And so it went. They were all learning that fighting in MTB's was no one-man job. There was little chance for hero stuff. Each officer, and each man, knew that the most efficient PT boat was one in which all eleven of the officers and crew worked together, pitching in on the job that needed to be done without waiting to be told what to do.

The boys were learning, too, that good PT fighting tactics called for teamwork between the different *boats* of a squadron, as well as between the men on each boat. In their classrooms, using small models of PT boats and enemy battleships, they worked out the fighting tactics and formations they would most frequently use in actual combat. Sometimes the PT's would work together as a division, each one rushing in to give the enemy its fatal sting. Under other conditions one PT in a division would be the "sacrifice" boat, speeding by to divert the enemy's attention so that the other two PT's could rush in for the kill.

Carrying out these tactics during daytime under-way cruises was not very difficult. But the boys knew that the time had come to find out whether they could operate with the same precision at night—which is the time PT's usually attack. As the Commanding Officer once remarked, "The first step is to become letter-perfect in PT tactics in daytime maneuvers. But unless you can carry out the same tactics without a hitch on night attacks, your first sortie against the enemy may well become a suicide mission!" The boys had never forgotten this warning.

135

Late one afternoon, as the Ensigns from Hut 27 were on their way over to the mess hall, the Base loud-speaker echoed its raucous "Now hear this!" The student officers paused almost automatically, waiting for the announcement. It might simply be an order directing someone to report to the O.D. But it might be something that was meant for all of them—and, this time, it was.

"Now hear this!" the Duty Officer repeated. "All student officers in Division A, and all enlisted men in Division F, will report to the docks at 1900 for under-way torpedo practice." He repeated the order.

"Well, this is it, fellows!" Bill Warner said as they continued on their way to the mess hall. "That's us. It will be dusk at 1900. I guess that means no shut-eye for us tonight."

"Join the PT Boat Squadrons for low-cost luxury cruises!" Bob Reed kidded, as though he were a barker trying to drum up customers for a sight-seeing motor launch at a summer resort. "Don't miss the thrilling speed-boat ride. The boat leaves in just a few minutes—covers all points of interest. See Japan in cherry-blossom time! Sail without a care under the tropical moon—"

"Cut it out!" Don Allen begged. "Tropical moon, my eye! Look at that sky!"

One glance at the black scudding clouds told them that there would be no moon that night! The bay was already flecked with whitecaps. They'd be lucky, they knew, if the rain held off until they actually got under way.

HEADING DOWN THE BAY for torpedo practice "outside."

"They sure picked the night for it!" Don Allen said.

As a matter of fact, the order for night-attack operations had not been a complete surprise to the student officers. That afternoon they had seen a Coast Guard cutter headed down Narragansett Bay toward open water "outside." This was usually a sure sign that two divisions of MTB's would take up the chase toward dusk—for this ship often acted as the target boat on night-attack operations.

Heading out into the ocean, well in advance of the PT Boat Squadrons, she would choose a secret destination and make for it, playing "hare" for the swift, relentless "hounds" of the sea—the PT boats. It then became the job of the PT's to locate their prey and "sink" her, using practice-run torpedoes. Just where they would find the cutter no one knew. Usually she steamed along a course somewhere in the ocean within a radius of twenty-five miles. Hunting her down on a gusty, moonless, pitch-dark night was like trying to find a needle in a haystack—blindfolded.

The lights were beginning to flick on in huts all over the Base as the two divisions of officers and men gathered on the docks shortly before seven o'clock that evening. The deep drumming of the PT's warming up their engines told them that it was almost time to cast off. There were six of the Mosquitoes being readied to get under way.

Bob Reed, Bill Warner, and Don Allen clambered aboard PT 176, which was skippered by Lieutenant

138

Moran. With them were several seamen who had gone out as part of their team in the past: Fox, radioman; Gribbin, torpedoman; West, quartermaster; and "Cat-eye" Daniels, a seaman, second class, who seemed to be gifted with almost superhuman night vision. All the skippers liked to have Daniels aboard as lookout, for he could spot an almost invisible target on the blackest night. "Cat-eye" claimed he was born with eyes like that. The others suspected that his remarkable night vision was the result of eating carrots. He practically lived on them! At any rate Bob was glad when he saw Daniels boarding PT 176. It increased their chances of being the first to spot the target.

Promptly at seven o'clock the two divisions of MTB's swung out into the bay and streaked southward toward the open sea. As they headed into the wind, an extraordinarily large wave crashed into the cockpit, soaking them all thoroughly. Luckily the boys had followed the skipper's example and had put on their oilskins before donning their kapok life jackets.

"We're likely to have heavy going outside tonight," Lieutenant Moran had said. "The rain is going to hold off awhile, I think; but there'll be a heavy swell that may cause us some trouble."

Turning the helm over to the quartermaster, he looked over the men who were under his command and started to assign them to their posts.

"When we get outside," he said, "we'll fall into echelon formation and sweep the area for a distance of twenty miles in each direction. PT 180 will be the lead boat in our formation," he continued.

He explained in detail how they would proceed, in a staggered formation—first PT 180, then PT 176, and finally PT 182—each boat separated from the next by a distance of about three hundred yards. The second division would sweep the area in the other direction, also in echelon formation. Somewhere in that area the cutter was hiding from them and, by combing the entire section methodically, they were sure to find her—they hoped!

"We'll proceed at about eighteen knots, with mufflers on," Lieutenant Moran explained. "The cutter does about twelve knots—maybe even less, tonight. The idea is to sneak in on the target slowly, if possible. And after we've fired our fish we'll sneak out again—unless we're discovered by the enemy. In that case the man at the helm will gun his engines and execute that well-known naval maneuver called 'getting the heck out of here!' Now, then, Reed will take the helm. Warner, man the torpedo director. Allen, down into the chartroom, as navigator. You will plot our course according to previous instructions."

He ran his eye over the faces grouped about him in the darkness of the cockpit. The lights from the instrument panel gave off a dim glow, just enough so that he could distinguish one man from another.

"Hello, Cat-eye," he grinned as he picked out Daniels. "Up forward with you—as lookout. Fox, take over the radio and communications. And you, Gribbin, will be tor-

140

pedoman. Is everything clear? Very well. Take over!"

The second division of MTB's had already veered off to the east and had been completely swallowed up in the darkness. PT 180 was swinging off and leading the formation in a westerly direction.

Bob Reed, at the helm, had his hands full as he stepped up his r.p.m.'s and tried to hold his place in the tight echelon formation. Now they were plowing through six-foot waves, but PT 176 was handling magnificently.

The seamen were readying the torpedo tubes, which were swung out at a slight angle for instant action. Contrary to the skipper's prediction, big drops of rain were now pelting down, making the poor visibility even worse. But, with engines muffled, the three PT's plowed along through the waves, all eyes piercing the wet blackness for a glimpse of the target vessel.

"It would help if they'd send up a flare!" Bob said jokingly to the seaman who stood beside him.

"It sure would!" the sailor replied. "They're not very obliging tonight."

The westerly run was uneventful. Several times Bob thought he saw the hulk of the Coast Guard cutter looming up to port or starboard. But each time he found that his eyes were playing him tricks.

At the end of the first hour and a half the lead boat signaled through the darkness for the formation to make the return sweep. The three Mosquitoes circled around and came about on the new course slightly farther out.

Ten minutes more passed. Then it happened!

"There she is—off our port bow!" Daniels cried.

The radioman was given the word to signal the other two boats, giving them the traditional battle order—"Boat captains take charge"—and the three PT's broke out of echelon formation, following the plan they had agreed upon earlier.

"The enemy has sighted us!" Bob sang out, as the searchlight from the cutter suddenly pierced the gloom, sweeping over each of the attacking PT's. The cutter was still about five hundred yards ahead, several points off the port bow of the lead boat.

Now the PT's, with mufflers wide open, were preparing to close in for the attack. Since they had been discovered, there was no longer any possibility of a sneak attack. Nor was there any advantage to be gained by stealth. This was purely a hit-and-run operation where speed, accuracy, and expert boat handling would count.

The gunner's mate took his position behind Bill Warner, who was already bringing his torpedo director to bear on the target. In the darkness the faintly luminous numbers on the director were his only guide.

Bob grasped the throttles firmly, squinting through the spray and murk at the lead boat for his cue. Gribbin, the torpedoman, stood beside Tube Number 1, mallet in hand. In combat a PT crew does not rely entirely upon the electrical impulse sent by the torpedo-firing button. If salt spray has shorted the circuit, it becomes necessary for the

THE LEADING PT BOAT, executing a turn at high speed, lays down a smooth "roadway" for the others to follow.

torpedoman to whack the percussion head with a mallet to make certain that the torpedo gets away. So, just as an added precaution, the torpedoman usually whams the percussion head for good measure, the instant the button is pressed.

Now things started to happen—*fast!* PT 180 suddenly cut across their bow at terrific speed, her smoke-screen generators laying down a thick curtain of "soup." This was the move Bob had been waiting for. Pressing his throttles forward, he gave PT 176 hard right rudder; then he swung around in a hissing S curve straight into the smoke screen toward the target. Glancing back over his shoulder, he could see PT 182 coming on through their wake, her white "rooster tail" surging upward through the blackness of the night.

Bill, at the torpedo director, raised his hand.

"Stand by to fire!" he bellowed. Then came the order, *"Fire!"*

Bill pressed the firing button . . . and the torpedoman, at the same instant, brought his mallet down on the percussion head. There was a sharp explosion. The torpedo whizzed through its tube and hurtled into the water, streaking toward the ill-fated cutter.

Bob jammed his throttles full ahead and gave the PT hard left rudder. As he turned away, PT 182 rushed in and delivered its Sunday punch. Then it, too, executed a sizzling U turn right under the guns of the cutter, and roared off into the night.

Now, if ever, a PT boat needed the terrific power of its brute Packard engines! A "cold potato"—an engine which "conked out" on the getaway—would leave a PT boat helpless, completely at the mercy of the enemy's guns.

Bob glanced at his three r.p.m. dials. All three were knocking off a beautiful 2500. In a matter of seconds they would be back out of the smoke screen and in the clear, swallowed up in the darkness. Already the radioman was notifying Division 2 of their successful attack.

"Two direct hits," he flashed. "Close in and follow!" and he gave their position. "We are now returning to the Base."

The three PT's of Division 1 reformed and turned back toward home. In the distance they could see the small red flares in the practice heads of the two torpedoes they had fired. Guided by these flares, the pickup boat would soon recover the torpedoes and tow them back. As usual, all torpedoes had been set at a sufficient depth to pass safely underneath the target.

Lieutenant Moran, after directing the quartermaster to take the helm for the run back, complimented the officers and men for carrying out their first night-attack mission so successfully. But there was not much time for idle conversation. By now the wind had whipped up to almost gale force, and the rain was coming down in sheets.

As they beat their way toward the more sheltered waters of the bay, Bob regretted that he had had to give over the helm—for a very selfish reason. The skipper of a PT boat

145

has one slight advantage over the rest of his men in heavy going. He stands on a heavy sponge-rubber mat which absorbs much of the shock, as the boat pounds into the seas!

Huddled in the cockpit, the officers and men were now holding on for dear life as PT 176 shuddered again and again under the impact of the tremendous waves.

"Up off your heels, men!" Lieutenant Moran cautioned them. "And hang on!"

Bob was thankful for the extra padding afforded by the thick kapok life jacket he wore over his foul-weather gear. Time and again he thumped against the side of the cockpit so hard that it almost knocked the wind out of him. But he found that the skipper was right. By standing in a semicrouch, knees flexed slightly and all the weight on the balls of his feet, he could take the worst of it without being bounced about too violently. He had heard of PT boatmen coming in with fractured bones and cut faces. The important thing was to hang on—*and he did!*

By the time the plunging PT rounded the headland, several of the boys were sick. But fortunately everyone was too busy to pay any attention to such unhappy souls. It was just one of the things that sometimes happened on a PT boat. Bob himself had that familiar pea-green feeling as they swung north into the bay. He heaved a sigh of relief as the quartermaster increased his r.p.m.'s for the relatively smooth run back up to Melville. The worst was over.

146

HEAVY GOING doesn't bother a PT boat much. It takes mighty big waves to even slow them down.

Half an hour later the three PT's turned into the lagoon and were soon secured alongside their docks.

With fingers stiffened from clenching the handrail, Bob clumsily unlaced his life jacket and peeled it off. He looked at his watch. It was 1:05 A.M. But he didn't mind the lateness of the hour. At least the firm planking of the dock was underfoot—firm planks that were no longer pitching and heaving!

"What's the matter, skipper?" Bill Warner asked as they started from the docks up the path toward the huts. "You look a bit on the queasy side, it seems to me."

"Oh, I'm all right," Bob lied. "Just sleepy, I guess."

"Yeah, I know!" Don Allen chimed in. "You're just sleepy—and how that bed is tossing!"

"Say, Don," Bill Warner broke in, "how does that old song go—remember?" And he started singing, badly off key:

"We were sailing along, on Moonlight Bay . . ."

Bob groaned.

"Have a heart, Bill!" he begged. "I'll never again make a crack about moonlight cruises—I give you my word!"

The Bougainville Express

Things happened fast at Melville, those last few weeks. There was much still to be done, and many things still to be learned—and time was short. The period of training was almost over for Ensign Bob Reed and his classmates.

Some of the boys had already put in their requests for combat duty in areas where they wanted most to go.

"Not that it will do much good," Bob remarked as he filed his request. "They'll send us where we're needed most."

"But there's no harm in trying," Ted Butler said. "So here goes."

Bob and Bill Warner requested active duty in Squadron X, based in the South Pacific. Because they had hit it off pretty well together during their training, they wanted to get into the same squadron, if possible, when they left Melville. Some of the other boys, too, requested South Pacific duty. A few, for various reasons, put in for duty in United States coastal waters, or in new squadrons which were forming for Alaskan bases, or in the Mediterranean.

It was not an easy choice to make; for wherever there were PT Boat Squadrons, reports that came in told of the terrific job they were doing. Whichever squadron a new officer or man selected, he could be certain of seeing plenty of action!

More and more of the instructors at Melville were now officers and men who had done a tour of duty and had returned to help train new PT boat crews.

These fellows had been in the thick of it. They knew the score.

One of them was a radioman, first class, by the name of Tom Hart. Hart had served under Bulkeley and had helped General MacArthur escape from Corregidor to Australia in a PT boat. Later he had seen plenty of action in a PT Squadron off the Solomons.

One of his most exciting experiences took place off Guadalcanal. Shortly after his return to Melville, Hart spoke one evening in the auditorium to give the new men a firsthand account of what they might expect when they went out with their own squadrons.

"Things were getting sort of tough for us right after the Marines kicked the Japs off Guadalcanal and took over Henderson Field," he explained. "Every night the Japs would send over a naval task force. They'd stand offshore and plaster our installations with everything they had."

He said that the Americans had a nickname for the Jap task force. They called it the "Bougainville Express" be-

150

cause it set out from its base on the Jap-held island of Bougainville, in the Solomons.

One pitch-dark night, just as the Japs started to blast the Marines' positions, the American PT boats swept in.

"We didn't know how many ships the enemy had, or what kind," the radioman continued. "But it wasn't long before we found out. From the flash of the guns we picked out a Jap battleship, several heavy cruisers, and eight destroyers. And then we realized the spot we were in. Our squadron of PT's had streaked right through the destroyer screen. We were surrounded by the enemy!"

In a situation like that there was only one thing to do —and the PT men did it. Before the Japs knew what had happened, the deadly mosquito boats let go their torpedoes and streaked out to sea again.

"The only hit we were sure of was a cruiser," Hart said. "We saw it sinking, aflame, as we turned and gunned our engines. But that was just the start of the mess," he continued.

"Those Jap destroyers picked us out with their search-lights and took up the chase—two of them chasing each PT boat. Our gunners shot out some of the lights; but, even so, we were behind the eight ball. We were giving those Packard engines of ours everything they'd take. They were turning over 2750 r.p.m.'s." Someone in the audience gave a low whistle of amazement. The radioman grinned. "Sure, I know that your engineering manuals tell you that the engines are set for only 2500 r.p.m.'s

—but, you see, those engines knew they were being chased!"

That remark brought a laugh. For everyone in the audience knew that a PT boat, in a tight corner, isn't just fast—it simply disappears!

Radioman Hart pointed out that team play is the most effective strategy for PT boats.

"It's no use trying to torpedo a destroyer that's coming right at you," he said. "The best move is to pull it out of position where your teammates can take a crack at it. We happened to know that there was another squadron of PT's on patrol near by, so we led those destroyers a merry chase—away from the task force."

Acting as decoys, the first PT's drew the Jap destroyers out into the open. When the second squadron caught sight of the quarry, it rushed in, unleashed its torpedoes, and sank four of the destroyers.

"Five units of the Mikado's fleet became dead ducks that night," Hart concluded. "The rest of them turned tail and ran for it. The U.S. Marines were a happier bunch of men after the PT's helped take the pressure off them. That night the Nip task force kissed Guadalcanal good-by for good."

He stressed again the importance of teamwork in PT tactics.

"The signals are called when we leave the docks—and, from then on, each boat, and each man, is on his own," he explained. "When things start to pop, it's like open-field

152

IN PATROL FORMATION, a squadron of PT boats on the prowl for enemy warships. The wake they leave behind them is evidence of their terrific power.

running, in football, after you recover a fumble. Your interference clears the way for you without waiting for signals. This is the sort of game where you can't wait for coaching from the side lines and you make up your own rules as you go along. Most of the rules aren't even in the book."

The Senior Instructor, who was sitting on the speaker's platform, interrupted to ask what sort of fighters the Japs were.

"They're tough bozos, sir," the radioman replied. "We soon learned that they don't know the meaning of fair play. They're out to win at any cost—and most of them would rather die for the Mikado than surrender. Never give a Jap an even break. He's a deceitful, treacherous, desperate foe."

He added that some of the captured Japs in the Solomons zone had their pockets stuffed with paper money, printed in Japan, bearing the English inscription "One Pound Note."

"They were so sure of successfully invading Australia that the soldiers had been supplied with 'Made in Japan' British money for spending in the shops of Sydney and Darwin," Hart explained. "Looks as though we upset their timetable when we derailed the Bougainville Express!"

Following radioman Hart's talk, a Lieutenant Jackson addressed the boys. He, too, had served in the South Pacific and had come back to Melville for temporary duty

ON THE ALERT to meet any menace, a squadron of speedy
PT boats streaks along on protective patrol with guns poised
for action.

as an instructor in PT boat tactics.

"The exploits which radioman Hart has told you about his squadron are true," Lieutenant Jackson said. "I know. I was there. But Hart was too modest to tell you the *whole* story—so I'm going to pick up where he left off. And what I'm going to tell you is of particular interest to you young commissioned officers who will soon be going out as captains and executive officers on your own MTB's."

He paused and his eye swept over the boys in the assembly room.

"Maybe you won't like this, but you'd better—because it's straight from the shoulder," he continued. "There are no heroes in a PT Boat Squadron. The boats themselves are the heroes. *No one man* stands out above the others. Each officer and member of the crew is just a plain American guy, in there pitching his best for his teammates. In the PT Squadrons—as in the whole U.S. Navy—the backbone and guts of the entire operation are the enlisted men. Never forget that! There must be discipline and respect for officers, yes. But, when you're in there delivering your Sunday punch, each man is on his own—and how good a teammate he is determines whether you come through or whether it's taps for your PT boat and every man on her.

"That night the boys smashed up the Bougainville Express, two shells from one of the destroyers came so close to Hart's PT that almost all the men aboard, including both officers, were knocked down. They lay there half stunned, clinging to whatever support they could find."

Lieutenant Jackson then related how Hart was the first man to come to. With Jap shells still whining uncomfortably close, he sized up the situation and sprang to the helm. Taking over the controls, he laid down a trail of smoke and jammed the PT through to join the other boats in his squadron.

"He got out of there so fast he almost took on some altitude!" the Lieutenant said with a chuckle. "That was a close call and it shows what I mean by teamwork. I might add that all hands were back in action the next day. It takes plenty of stuff to knock out a PT man for keeps!"

From talks like these, as well as from discussions in the classrooms with officers and men back from the combat zones, the Ensigns began to get a clearer picture of some of the things they would be up against as PT officers.

In the torpedo shop, one day, a torpedoman by the name of Wilson told the boys some of the experiences he had gone through as a PT man in the Solomons area.

He said that their gunners became so expert at picking off the searchlights on Jap warships with their machine guns that the Japs finally gave up using their lights, even when they wanted very much to spot the PT boats in the darkness.

"But for real excitement," Wilson told them, "just wait until you're strafed by a formation of Zeros!"

And he related how, when it happened the first time, their skipper outwitted the diving planes by zigging in S curves with his throttles wide open. All the time the PT's .50 caliber guns were whamming away at the Zeros. Most of the Jap pilots had a very healthy respect for the tracers streaming at them and would pull out of their dives before getting close enough to fire their cannon.

Every now and then the PT gunners would score a hit on one of the planes, some of which crashed into the sea with smoke pluming back from their motors.

"One plane we hit kept right on coming," Wilson said. "It looked like a suicide dive. Then, all of a sudden, there was a flash and a ball of fire. The next moment the plane had completely disappeared in mid-air!"

As Bob Reed and his classmates listened to these stories of action in the Pacific, they sometimes wondered just how *they* would feel the first time under fire. One night as they were sprawled on their bunks "shooting the breeze" in Hut 27, Lieutenant Jackson dropped in for a chat and to get better acquainted with the young officers who would soon be leaving.

After they had talked a while, Bob said, "Lieutenant, before you came in, some of us were trying to figure out just how a fellow really feels when shells are landing all around his PT boat—especially if he's never been under fire before."

Lieutenant Jackson smiled.

"I'll answer that one gladly, Reed," he said. "The first

WHAT A TEAM! U. S. Navy PT boats and U. S. Army
fighter planes make a combination that the enemy has learned
to fear.

time it happens—and *every* time it happens—you'll be plenty scared. I know *I* was; and I think I can speak for the rest of the men, too. You'll be afraid—but that doesn't mean you're a coward. Fear is a natural instinct when you're in danger. The fact that you're afraid doesn't matter. It's what you *do* that counts.

"After a few seconds," he continued, "there comes a certain point when you almost stop thinking. That's when your instinct takes over. Then, because of the instruction and drills you've had here at Melville, it becomes almost second nature for you to do exactly the right thing. You'll swing into action almost automatically and you'll probably do the job so well that you'll find yourself winding up as a blooming hero! At least, to be perfectly honest, that's how I got *my* decoration," he added modestly.

"You won't find much glamour in your job, fellows," he warned them. "There's nobody in the grandstands watching you and cheering you on. It's going to mean sweat and drudgery and sleepless nights and things that no civilized man enjoys seeing or taking part in. But the PT Squadrons are a wonderful branch of the service. You'll find that you're working and fighting with the best shipmates in the Navy."

He told the boys that they would probably become very much attached to their own boat.

"We all do," he said. "We used to call our PT the 'Ugly Duckling' of the squadron. She was battle-scarred and showed that she'd taken a lot of punishment, but we loved her. One day, long after she had accounted for more than her share of Jap destroyers and shipping, she was knocked out in combat. We stuck with her to the end, but finally had to abandon her. We boarded a U.S. sub, which was near by, and went below."

He said that the skipper of the submarine asked permission to sink the crippled PT boat, for there was no hope of salvaging her. Reluctantly Lieutenant Jackson agreed.

"So the sub's deck gun opened up on the 'Ugly Duckling,'" he continued. "Each shot sounded like a giant door being slammed topside. My gunner's mate was a farmboy from Virginia, named Lem Axton. Each time that submarine's gun let go, he flinched.

"'You know,' he said, 'that boat was just like an ornery old mule I used to have. She was always getting into trouble, and I've cussed her every day I've been on her. But when the time comes for her to go, it almost makes you cry!'

"And that's the way we all felt about that PT," Lieutenant Jackson concluded.

Completely carried away by the memory of experiences he had been through, the seasoned PT boat officer related still another incident to his small but eager audience. It had to do with a PT boat that had been hit once by a Jap cruiser. But that night, under cover of darkness, it crept up on the enemy cruiser and fired its one remaining torpedo with great care—and the fish struck home.

"That PT had two strikes on her before she entered the game, but she won out," Lieutenant Jackson said. "Then she came limping home and later was put into first-class fighting condition again. The cruiser, we found out later, traveled only a few miles before she was beached and deserted.

"That PT skipper never did any bragging, and he can never talk about it now—for he was lost in action a few weeks later. But he had the idea that he *could*—that he *had* to—do some fast pitching, and he did it.

"He was always looking forward to the day when new men and new boats would be coming to carry on the fight. Replacing men like him will be a great job and an inspiring challenge to you fellows—but it's up to you to do it.

"The Jap is nobody's fool. He can hit any kind of pitching. But with each man covering his position and covering it well, we are certainly going to win. We've got to win, because the enemy is staking his life. But he's up against better men than he is—and better fighting equipment. And, by the Almighty, we *will* win!"

No one in the hut said a word for several minutes after Lieutenant Jackson had finished speaking.

Finally he glanced at his watch and exclaimed, "Say! I've kept you men from boning up for your final exams tomorrow. I'll be shoving along now—it's almost time for 'Lights Out.'"

The boys rose to their feet as the officer got up to leave. He shook hands with each of them.

162

ACTION IN THE SOUTH PACIFIC! A PT speeds back
to its base with the good news that the Jap fleet now has one
less destroyer!

"Good luck, men, if I don't see you again before you leave Melville," he said earnestly. "Something tells me you've got the stuff our PT Squadrons are looking for. *And how they need you!*"

He turned and walked out of the hut.

TOO FAST TO CATCH! The Navy's hit-and-run PT boats have
sunk a staggering total of Axis tonnage.

Farewell to Melville

One morning, three days later, the marks for the final exams were posted. The Ensigns gathered around the bulletin board to find out the score.

Bob Reed ran his eye down the list to the R's and found his name. He breathed a sigh of relief when he saw a fat 3.80 chalked up against it. Bill Warner pulled down a 3.80, too . . . Don Allen a 3.85 . . . and so on. The others were safely over the hump, also. Not a man who still remained in the class had failed to pass his final exams.

"That's a load off my mind, believe me!" Bob exclaimed. "I was certain that I had one of my navigation equations in the test fouled up like a Chinese fire drill."

"Maybe so—but you made the grade," Bill replied. "So did we all. What's the pitch now, guys?"

"Well, we have a class on Tactics in ten minutes," Don Allen reminded them. "We'd better lay a course for Hut 80."

They started to walk over to the classroom hut.

"At mess this morning the scuttle butt was that today would be our last," Bob remarked. "I was sitting next to Lieutenant Walker, the Communications instructor, and

THE LAST HURDLE—final exams! Tomorrow—or the next
day—they'll be full-fledged PT boat officers.

I asked him if we were going to get our orders today."

"Well, what did he say?" one of the boys asked.

"He just made a crack about the weather and got up and left," Bob replied.

"Well, I'm not going to pack up yet, just on the strength of that," Bill said. "But I wouldn't be surprised if we got our orders today, just the same."

And that, as it turned out, was exactly what happened.

The boys were in the midst of a lesson in PT fighting tactics—moving small wooden models of the boats in a new attack formation—when the door of the classroom hut opened and in walked the Executive Officer of the Base, Lieutenant Commander Waring.

"Well, men," he greeted them, as he put a bundle of scrolls down on the instructor's desk, "the time has come for you to leave Melville. I am about to give you your diplomas and, even more important, your orders for combat duty."

He paused, and motioned to the student officers to come closer and form a group around his desk.

"There's a war on, men—and a grim job waiting to be done out where you're going. So this won't be a very fancy graduation," he continued in a friendly tone of voice. "I'm not even going to make a speech. I have nothing to tell you that you haven't already heard from the Commanding Officer and from the men who have come back to us from the combat zones. We know that each of you will live up

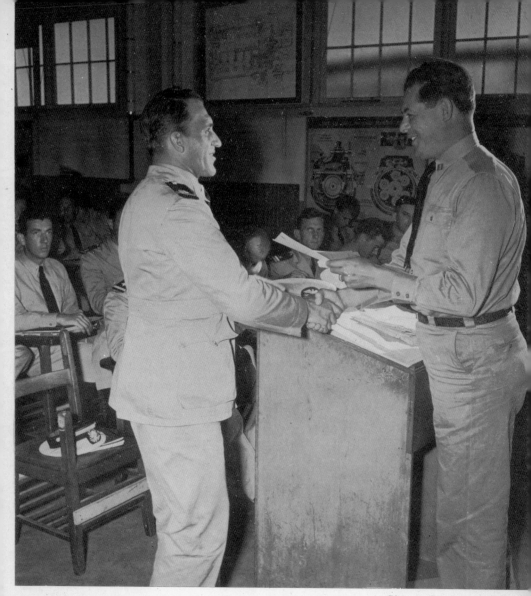

Photo by Carroll Van Ark

THERE'S NO TIME for fancy graduation ceremonies at Melville! *Above:* An Ensign proudly receives his diploma and orders for combat duty.

to the highest PT traditions."

One by one he read off the names of the graduates who were in the classroom. As each man's name was read, the Ensign advanced to the desk to receive his diploma and orders.

At the end of the informal ceremony Lieutenant Commander Waring shook hands with the new PT officers, wished them good luck, and left the hut. As the door closed, the boys excitedly opened their scrolls.

Bob Reed looked at his.

"Be it known," it stated, "that Ensign Bob Reed has successfully completed his course of training at the Motor Torpedo Boat Squadrons Training Center and . . ."

That was the diploma. Bob slipped it into his pocket and opened the other scroll, which contained his orders. His eye skimmed rapidly down toward the middle of the page. There it was!

"Hey, Bill!" he shouted. "I got my first choice! How'd you make out?"

"On the beam!" Bill grinned. "I got mine, too. That means we'll be in the same squadron!"

Bob read his orders now, more carefully, to make certain of exactly what he was to do. The orders went as follows:

"When directed by the Commanding Officer, Motor Torpedo Boat Squadrons Training Center, Melville, R. I., you will regard yourself detached from temporary duty under instruction at the above Base, and will proceed via

170

government or commercial air transport to San Francisco, California, from which port you will proceed by the first available transportation, including air, to the Port in which the Commander of MTB Squadron X may be and, upon your arrival, report to said Commander for duty."

Most of the boys had succeeded in getting their first choice, it turned out. And, now that their training was over, they were all anxious to shove off.

"How long will it take you to pack your gear, Bob?" asked Bill as they walked back to Hut 27.

"About five minutes," Bob replied. "And I'm thinking the same thing you are. If we can catch that noon bus, we can get to New York in time to see a show tonight before we hop that plane for the coast."

"Right!" Bill agreed. "I'll see how many of the gang will join us."

A few minutes later the boys came out of Hut 27 and started up the path to the H.Q. hut to check out for good. Bob Reed dropped slightly behind the others. He looked out over blue Narragansett Bay—*for the last time,* he thought to himself a little sadly.

Three PT's were sliding out of the lagoon, their Packard motors blasting back their defiant roar against the shore. For a brief moment Bob almost wished he could be under way—just once more—at Melville. But that, he knew, was all behind him now.

As he turned his eyes from the bay on which he had spent so many thrill-packed hours, he thought of Squadron X—far off in the South Pacific—and of the gallant PT men who had gone before him.

Somewhere on an island base—more than ten thousand miles away—the teammates in the fighting crew of a United States Navy PT boat were waiting for their new teammate and skipper.

Their new teammate and skipper . . . Ensign Bob Reed!